GW00384643

impact
WORKBOOK
1

SERIES EDITORS
JoAnn (Jodi) Crandall
Joan Kang Shin

NATIONAL GEOGRAPHIC LEARNING | CENGAGE Learning

Australia • Brazil • Mexico • Singapore • United Kingdom • United States

Unit 1
Life in the City

1 **Find ten vocabulary words.** Then write the correct words to complete each sentence.

opankskyscrapersnubckbuniquenvkvufkvkfvunusualkbebfbcapitaluffjfilujlf
urbanmbdhwfulitruralubsjjshapeyeplangubbodesigninbotrtowernosid

1. People often talk about the differences between _____ life and
   _____ life. My friend is _____ because she
   lives for six months in the city and six months in the countryside.

2. I have another friend who has a very special window in his bedroom. The window is in
   the roof and has the _____ of a star. It's like sleeping under the
   stars! The _____ is _____ because he made
   it himself—nobody else has one like it!

3. Living in a _____ city is exciting. When I get a job, I
   _____ to live in Paris or Ottawa or Rome.

4. Is there a city in the world that doesn't have tall buildings or
   _____ ? Maybe, but every airport must have a communications
   _____ to help planes.

2 **Listen.** Write the number of the sentence that goes with each picture. **TR: 2**

a.

b.

c.

d.

e.

f.

3 **Listen.** Then read and check **T** for *True* or **F** for *False*. Rewrite the false statements to make them true. **TR: 3**

	T	F
1. Renato is an architect.	☐	☐
2. He designs skyscrapers.	☐	☐
3. Renato's design for a city has areas only for people.	☐	☐
4. In Renato's city, cars travel above residents' heads.	☐	☐
5. Renato's design is only for older people.	☐	☐
6. Renato's city design is safe for the residents.	☐	☐
7. The bicycle tracks are high up with the cars.	☐	☐
8. Renato's city is expensive to build.	☐	☐

_____

_____

_____

_____

GRAMMAR

Simple present: General statements

Architects **design** new buildings for cities.	She **studies** the plans for the new capital.
The city's design **includes** a lot of green spaces.	The road **goes** next to an indoor park.
This tall tower **doesn't look** new.	The skyscraper **has** a garden inside.

To form the simple present, use the infinitive without *to*. *I/You/We/They* **design** unusual buildings. Note that with *he/she/it*, we add **-s** to the verb: *He/She* **designs** a new skyscraper. *It* **looks** amazing. To make a negative sentence, use *don't* or *doesn't*.

The spelling of some verbs changes after adding **-s** or **-es**. Add **-es** to verbs such as *cross* → *cross**es***, *wash* → *wash**es***, *watch* → *watch**es***. For verbs that end in *y*, drop the *y* and add **-ies**: *study* → *stud**ies***.

Some verbs are irregular: *go* → *go**es***, *do* → *do**es***, *have* → **has**.

4 **Listen.** Circle the verb you hear. Then listen again to check your answers. **TR: 4**

1. Capital cities **has** / **have** large public areas.

2. Children often **play** / **plays** in city parks.

3. An architect **teach** / **teaches** how to design buildings.

4. People **doesn't** / **don't** walk on this sidewalk.

5. Huge mountains **surround** / **surrounds** the capital city.

6. In winter the city park **closes** /**close** early.

7. She **study** / **studies** unusual architecture in Denmark.

8. The bridge **doesn't** / **don't** go to the sports center.

5 **Write.** Fill in the blanks with the correct simple-present form.

1. In Bogotá, people sometimes _____ (use) the highway to bicycle.

2. Residents _____ (like) to relax by the stream.

3. Architects _____ (not design) skyscrapers for rural areas.

4. A new bridge _____ (cross) the highway.

5. People _____ (need) green spaces in capital cities.

6. Sometimes architects _____ (plan) buildings with parks on the roof.

7. In urban areas, people _____ (not enjoy) crowded sidewalks.

8. My village _____ (have) a water tower.

9. A major highway _____ (connect) two big cities.

10. The stream _____ (not go) through the city.

6 **Write about a city you know.** Use some of the words in the box.

Things:	architecture	bridge	highway	shape	sidewalk	skyscraper	tower
Describing words:	concrete	indoor	outdoor	rural	unique	unusual	urban
Verbs:	be	construct	cross	design	have	need	plan

_____

_____

_____

_____

_____

_____

7 **Draw a plan of your city.** Use a separate piece of paper. Practice talking about the details of your plan with your classmates or teacher.

Desire* Paths

desire *v.* to want something
n. the feeling of wanting something
Note: In the reading title, *desire* is used as an adjective.

[1] Everybody has seen one, most people have walked on one, and perhaps you started a new one. We may not know the name, but these paths are called "desire paths." These are paths, tracks, or sidewalks made by people or animals walking on the grass to move quickly from one concrete sidewalk to another. For example, we see these paths in urban spaces where people don't use the sidewalks, but take a shortcut through green land, parks, and gardens.

[2] So why do people decide to walk on the green grass and not on the sidewalks? Sometimes the architect's plan for urban spaces isn't the best. Residents, people like you and me, who use the outdoor areas every day know the best and quickest way to walk from one place to another.

[3] The problem is that we destroy the grass when we make a desire path. Also, these new tracks get wet and dirty easily. Concrete is cleaner. We know that we need to protect our green spaces, but we also need to move from place to place quickly.

[4] Perhaps we need better designers and architects to plan our sidewalks and urban green spaces. They should ask local people and pay attention to what residents want.

9 **Answer the questions.** Write the number of the paragraph on the line.

_____ 1. Which paragraph tells us a definition of desire paths?

_____ 2. Which paragraph tells us about problems with desire paths?

_____ 3. Which paragraph describes the reasons for desire paths?

_____ 4. Which paragraph discusses possible solutions to the problems?

10 **Complete the diagram.** Read the text again and make notes in the boxes.

Desire paths

Reasons
1.
2.

Problems
1.
2.

11 **Think about the information from the texts in this unit.** You've read about desire paths and a plan to make London into a new type of national park. Read the sentences. Do you agree with these ideas? Check (✓) the box if you agree. Write a question mark (**?**) if you're not sure. Mark (**X**) if you don't agree.

1. There's a lot of green space in my hometown. ☐

2. We need to protect green spaces in cities. ☐

3. I use desire paths. ☐

4. Concrete sidewalks are important. ☐

5. I feel happier when I spend time outdoors. ☐

6. The walk to my nearest park is too long. ☐

7. Architects should ask city residents about their ideas for green spaces. ☐

8. People don't have enough information about nature in urban areas. ☐

GRAMMAR

In and *on*: Expressing location

People walk **on** the grass and make new paths.	There aren't enough trees **in** cities.
There's a restaurant **on** top of the skyscraper.	We need more green spaces **in** urban areas.
I walk my dog **on** the sidewalk.	I like to relax **in** the park.

We use *in* and *on* to tell where something is. Use *in* to give the idea that things are inside something or in an area; for example, in buildings, cities, and countries. *People live in skyscrapers. There are many beaches in Rio de Janeiro. Rio de Janeiro is in Brazil. Brazil is a country in South America.*

Use *on* to tell that something is on the surface or on top of something else. We also use *on* with streets and roads. *They live on an island. Their house is on Broad Street. They often walk on the beach.*

12 **Circle the correct preposition.**

1. Cars don't go **on** / **in** sidewalks.

2. There are a lot of skyscrapers **in** / **on** big cities.

3. The Statue of Liberty is **on** / **in** an island.

4. You can find lot of green areas **in** / **on** the countryside.

5. Moscow is **in** / **on** Russia.

6. The Taj Mahal is **on** / **in** India.

7. The most popular Internet café is **on** / **in** Main Street.

8. The architect lives **in** / **on** Los Angeles.

9. Many residents of Rio de Janeiro like to relax **on** / **in** the beach.

10. There's a new restaurant **on** / **in** top of the building.

13 **Listen.** Draw a dot *in* or *on* each box according to the sentence you hear. **TR: 6**

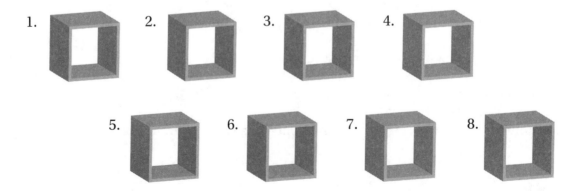

14 **Write.** Marta is in her first year at college. This is an e-mail to her younger brother. Read and fill in the blanks with *in* or *on*.

Hi Seba,

How are you? I'm fine now, after two days (1) _____ my new room at college. It's really cool here. Everybody can find me easily because my name is (2) _____ the door!

I don't know the town very well yet, but my building is (3) _____ Main Street, so everything is close. I see that there's a new park near my building. Guess what? It has a skateboard track (4) _____ the middle! So bring your skateboard when you come. I think you can fit it (5) _____ your bag, can't you? Here's a photo of the park.

I'm thinking of joining a club that does something called "Parkour." Have you heard of it? They also call it "urban free running" — running (6) _____ cities. Look it up on the Internet. There are some amazing videos!

Say hi to Mom and Dad, and see if you can visit me soon.

Bye for now!

Marta

15 **Think about the design of the neighborhood where you live.** Write at least six sentences using *in* and *on* and the words from the box. Practice talking about your neighborhood with your classmates or teacher.

bridge	highway	park	river	shopping mall	sidewalk	skyscraper

I live in a skyscraper in downtown Hong Kong.

_____

_____

_____

_____

WRITING

When we want to tell someone about a person, a place, or a thing, we often use descriptive words. Words such as *dirty*, *busy*, and *wet* are adjectives that go with nouns to paint a better picture in our mind. Notice how these descriptive words create different pictures in our mind.

- *Alexis skates on the **dirty** sidewalk.*
- *Alexis skates on the **busy** sidewalk.*
- *Alexis skates on the **wet** sidewalk.*

16 Organize

1. Your topic is a place that needs changing. Think of a place you know that has a problem. Maybe it's very small, too dry or wet, or maybe there's a lot of garbage there.

   In the first column, list three things you don't like about the place. Then, in the second column, think of how you can change each thing. Use descriptive words.

A place I don't like	My changes
school playground—broken bench	new, wooden bench

   Read your two lists and add more descriptive adjectives. Use a dictionary to help.

2. Plan your writing. You need an opening statement that describes the place and what the problem is. This will be your topic sentence. It helps the readers understand your idea. Write your topic sentence here:

   _____

   Next, you'll need a paragraph describing what the problem is, and a paragraph about what the place looks like after the change. Remember to use descriptive words to create a picture in your readers' minds.

17 Write

1. Go to page 21 in your book. Reread the model text and the descriptive words.
2. Write your first draft. Check for organization, content, punctuation, capitalization, and spelling.
3. Write your final draft. Share it with your teacher and classmates.

Now I Can . . .

talk about cities and different types of life in the city.

☐ Yes, I can!
☐ I think I can.
☐ I need more practice.

Write two sentences about urban life.

_____

_____

Write two sentences about green spaces in cities.

_____

_____

use the simple present to talk about general statements.

☐ Yes, I can!
☐ I think I can.
☐ I need more practice.

Write four sentences using the simple present form of any of the verbs from the box.
Two of your sentences should be negative.

| construct | design | explore | find | grow | live | need | pay | plan | use | walk |

_____

_____

_____

use *in* and *on* to express location.

☐ Yes, I can!
☐ I think I can.
☐ I need more practice.

Write four sentences about a place you know. Use *in* and *on*.

_____

_____

_____

write a description of a place in my neighborhood.

☐ Yes, I can!
☐ I think I can.
☐ I need more practice.

Use four or more descriptive words to write about a real place.

_____

_____

_____

Choose an activity. Go to page 90.

Unit 2
Amazing Jobs

1 **Draw.** Complete the maze by connecting all the words.

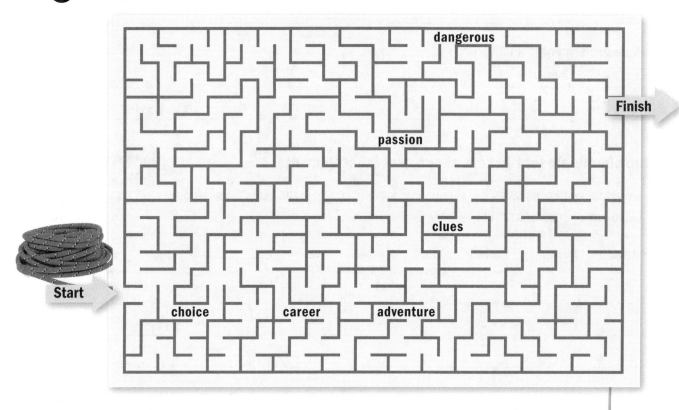

2 **Write.** Complete the sentences with the words from Activity 1.

1. She loves to cook something new every day. She has
   a _____ for cooking.

2. Guillermo has been an underwater archaeologist for many years.
   That's his _____ .

3. Would you like to work in an office or in an underwater cave?
   For me that's an easy _____ !

4. We had an amazing _____ in India! Every day we did something
   different. What a great place!

5. Divers take risks in difficult places. Their job can be _____ .

6. We had no _____ to help us find the ancient city ruins.

3 **Write.** Read each sentence and write the profession it describes.

> archaeologist   researcher

1. This person usually **works** in an **office**. _____researcher_____

2. This person usually doesn't **work** outdoors. _____

3. This worker **considers** what is true or false and writes a report. _____

4. This person **studies** history and sometimes finds lost objects. _____

5. This worker **trains** with a team for many weeks. _____

6. This person **works** alone at a computer most of the time. _____

7. Sometimes, this person's **profession** can be **dangerous**. _____

4 **Listen.** Match each speaker to a job from the box. Write the job on the line. **TR: 7**

> archaeologist   diver   office worker   researcher   ROV operator

1. _____   3. _____   5. _____

2. _____   4. _____

5 **Write.** Which profession in Activity 4 is your favorite? Least favorite? Complete the sentences with your own ideas.

1. A/an _____ is my favorite of these jobs because

_____ .

2. A/an _____ is my least favorite of these jobs because

_____ .

3. I'm not sure about the job of _____ _____ because

_____ .

GRAMMAR

Simple present questions and answers: Talking about routines

Does a water slide tester **travel** to different countries?	**Yes**, he **does**. / **No**, he **doesn't**.
Do water slide testers **get** any money?	**Yes**, they **do**. / **No**, they **don't**.
Do you **know** when a water slide isn't good?	**Yes**, I **do**. Sometimes the water **doesn't go** on some parts of the slide, or the design is not perfect, so I **stop** in the middle.
Where do water slide testers **work**?	We **work** in places such as hotels, theme parks, and cruise ships.

To form questions in the simple present, use **do/does** and the verb (infinitive without *to*). A short answer to these questions starts with **Yes** or **No,** and we repeat **do/does** or **doesn't/don't** but not the verb. ***Does*** *an underwater explorer* ***have*** *a dangerous job?* **Yes**, *he* **does**. Sometimes, we give additional information. ***Do*** *you* ***like*** *your office?* **No**, *I* **don't**. *It's too small.*

When we look for specific information, we start the question with question words (*where, what, when, why,* and so on). ***Where do*** *researchers* ***work****? They* ***work*** *in an office.*

6 **Read and match the questions with the answers.**
Write the letter on the line.

_____ 1. Does this man like his job?

_____ 2. Do people really do this job?

_____ 3. How much money does he earn?

_____ 4. Why do designers need to test slides?

_____ 5. Does he need special physical training?

a. about $30,000 a year

b. Yes, he does! He enjoys it a lot.

c. No, he doesn't. He just needs to be fit.

d. Yes, they do!

e. because water slides have to be safe and fun

7 **Listen.** Then complete the short answers. **TR: 8**

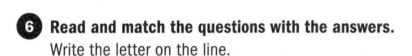

1. Yes, _____ I do _____ .

2. Yes, _____ .

3. No, _____ .

4. Yes, _____ .

5. No, _____ .

6. Yes, _____ .

8 **Write.** Use the words to ask questions.

1. he / speak / many languages _____

2. you / have / accidents _____

3. when / you / usually / work _____

4. he / need / interview _____

5. where / you / apply for / job _____

6. what / he / like / about his job _____

9 **Write.** Think about these unusual jobs. Imagine the answers to the questions.

1. What does a pet food tester do?

_____

_____

2. What does a dog surfing instructor do?

_____

_____

3. What does a golf ball diver do?

_____

_____

10 **Choose one unusual job from this unit.** Imagine you have an interview for that career. Ask and answer two questions.

Question: *What do underwater archaeologists do?*

Answer: *They study objects and places from the past, under water!*

Question 1: _____

Answer: _____

Question 2: _____

Answer: _____

Unlucky Days at Work

[1] When you choose an unusual career, like I did, you don't expect everything to be easy. I'm an underwater archaeologist, and things can go wrong. That's normal. Sometimes an advisor says that we might find bones in a cave, for example, but we arrive and it's empty. That tells me nobody lived there. So now we ask – why didn't anybody live in that cave? In this way we create new research and change a bad situation into something positive.

[2] When we explore an underwater cave, we work hard. We get up early, check our equipment, and drive for many hours. Then we get out and walk, carrying our heavy ropes and diving equipment. Like most people, we have to follow a schedule carefully. We can't spend too many hours diving.

[3] One time we got our measurements wrong. I went down into a cave on a 50-meter rope to check the cave. When I got near the bottom, the rope wasn't long enough. And then I saw that there was almost no water in the cave! I looked very funny with all my expensive diving equipment in a cave with no water! Anyway, underwater archaeology is my passion, and I like it better than commuting to an office.

1. Give an example from paragraph 1 of a problem that the author had.

_____

2. How are underwater archaeologists like many people? Give two examples.

_____

3. What is one problem the author describes in paragraph 3?

_____

12 **Read the text again.** Complete the chart for paragraph 1.

Paragraph 1	
Topic Sentence	
Supporting Details	
Concluding Sentence	

13 **Think about the information in this unit.** You've read about a photographer, a space scientist, and an underwater archaeologist. If you agree, check (✔) the sentence. If you don't agree, change the sentence so that it's true for you.

1. I want to be a professional photographer who works in the Himalayas.

   I don't want to be a professional photographer in the Himalayas. OR

   I want to be a professional photographer in the Caribbean.

2. Space science costs too much money. We don't need to learn about other planets.

   _____

3. Diving in a cave is probably the coolest job in the world.

   _____

4. Taking risks for your career is a bad idea.

   _____

5. Learning about the past helps us plan our future.

   _____

6. Explorers are important because we need to know more about our planet.

   _____

GRAMMAR

Possessives: Showing ownership

The **camera's** lens is broken.	**My** camera isn't working.
Thomas's dad is a photographer.	Is **his** mom a photographer, too?
NASA's new space telescope takes great pictures.	**Its** name is Hubble.
The **children's / boys'** password is new.	**Their** new password is "adventure."

To show that something belongs to a person or thing, we use these words: *my, your, his, her, its, our, their.*

We can also show possession by adding **'s** to a singular noun or to plural nouns that don't end in **s**: *The **diver's** job is interesting. **Women's** passion for diving isn't unusual.*

Add only an apostrophe (') to plural nouns that end in **s**: *photographers' cameras.* Add **'s** to words that end in **s**: *Mr. **Dickens's** house.*

14 **Listen for the possessives.** Circle the word you hear. **TR: 10**

1. **Jupiter's / Jupiter** moon might have water.

2. The **doctors' / doctor** plane is a flying hospital.

3. Are these **your / yours** oxygen tanks?

4. The **photographer's / photographer** camera is expensive.

5. All three **researcher / researchers'** data needs to be in one report.

6. The bicycle has lost **its / his** wheel.

7. Please order three **children / children's** meals.

15 **Write the possessive form for each noun.**

1. researcher   _researcher's_   5. office   _____

2. women   _____   6. Dickens   _____

3. bicycle   _____   7. puppies   _____

4. advisors   _____   8. house   _____

16 Complete the sentences. Use the correct words from the box.

my	your	his	her	its	our	their

1. Would you like to borrow ___my___ dictionary?

2. Oh no, _____ flight is late. We'll miss the connection in Madrid.

3. Excuse me, you dropped _____ ticket.

4. The divers carry _____ oxygen tanks.

5. Dr. Emily Park has to change _____ schedule this week.

6. His laptop isn't working now, so he has to recharge _____ battery.

7. Tony loves _____ work. He's an underwater photographer.

17 Listen. Then read and check **T** for *True* and **F** for *False*. Rewrite any false sentences to make them true. **TR: 11**

	T	F
1. Judy's job is to explore mountains.	☐	☐
2. Judy finds cool places in Dublin where animals also live.	☐	☐
3. Street art can change an ugly urban space into a more positive environment.	☐	☐
4. Animals need green spaces in cities.	☐	☐
5. A lot of young people in Dublin go to parks.	☐	☐
6. Judy wants young people to have fun and also experience nature.	☐	☐

WRITING

When we write good descriptive paragraphs, we want our readers to understand our ideas clearly. So, each paragraph needs a topic sentence, some details, and a concluding sentence.

> **steeplejack** –*n.* a person who climbs tall buildings to clean, paint, or repair them

18 Organize

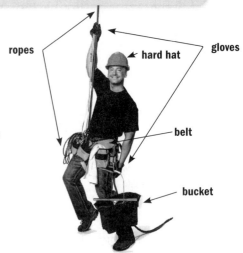

ropes · hard hat · gloves · belt · bucket

1. Your topic is to write a description of someone's daily routine for an unusual profession. Look through the unit for ideas on unusual jobs or do some research on the Internet. For example, you can write about the steeplejack in the photo.

2. Plan your writing. Your paragraph needs a title and should start with a topic sentence that describes the unusual job. Then write a few sentences about the daily routine of the person who has this unusual job. Finally, you will need a concluding sentence.

Use the chart to help you plan and list the important details of your paragraph. Think about details such as where the person works, what kind of equipment he or she needs to do the job, and what he or she does from day to day.

Title	
Topic Sentence	
Supporting Details	
Concluding Sentence	

19 Write

1. Go to p. 37 in your book. Reread the model text and the writing prompt.
2. Write your first draft. Check for organization, punctuation, capitalization, and spelling.
3. Check your final draft. Share it with your teacher and classmates.

Now I Can . . .

talk about unusual careers.

Describe one of these unusual careers.

□ Yes, I can!
□ I think I can.
□ I need more practice.

golf ball diver

pet food tester

_____

_____

_____

_____

use the simple present to ask and answer questions about routines.

□ Yes, I can!
□ I think I can.
□ I need more practice.

Complete the questions and answers with *do* or *does*, and a verb.

My uncle is a fortune cookie writer.

_____ he work every day? Yes, he _____ . / No, he _____ .

_____ you get cookies from him? Yes, I _____ . / No, I _____ .

Where _____ he _____ (work)? He _____ at home.

use possessives to show ownership.

□ Yes, I can!
□ I think I can.
□ I need more practice.

Change the nouns to possessives.

1. (Kenji) ____Kenji's____ advisor is a scientist. ____His____ advisor is a scientist.

2. (the dog) _____ food is very tasty. _____ food is very tasty.

3. (the men) _____ restaurant is underwater. _____ restaurant
   is underwater.

write a description of someone's daily routine.

□ Yes, I can!
□ I think I can.
□ I need more practice.

Title: _____

Topic sentence: _____

Details: _____

Conclusion: _____

Choose an activity. Go to p. 91.

Choose an activity. Go to p. 91.

Units 1–2 Review

1 **Read.** Choose the word that best completes the sentences.

1. Tammy's brothers and sisters don't like snakes, but she does.
   Her mother says that she's ____ in her family.
   (a.) unique   b. similar   c. normal

2. Tim goes to bed at 6:00 a.m. and wakes up at lunchtime. He works most nights.
   He's ____ because most people work during the day.
   a. unusual   b. common   c. normal

3. Ivan asks the photographer some questions. He's ____ her for his blog.
   a. researching   b. interviewing   c. considering

4. There are lots of parks and outdoor spaces in my city. I like living in
   a(n) ____ area.
   a. rural   b. urban   c. countryside

5. I love history, so I know what profession I want to study in college. I want to
   be an ____ .
   a. architect   b. animal researcher   c. archaeologist

6. Katerina climbs towers and skyscrapers in her work. She ____ every day.
   a. takes risks   b. applies for   c. constructs

2 **Listen.** Match each teenager to a career he or she might like. Write the number on the line. **TR: 12**

____ a. Steeplejack— travel the country; clean, repair tall buildings

____ b. Dog walker— outdoor spaces and parks; take dogs for walks

____ c. Personal trainer— sports center; help people keep fit, learn sports

____ d. Underwater photographer— seas around the world; taking photos

____ e. Researcher— home; collect information, interview, write reports

3 **Read.** Decide which answer (**a**, **b**, **c**, or **d**) best fits each blank space.

A Twenty-first Century Place to Live

My home is in Yangon, the old capital of Myanmar. Yangon (1) ____ city center is changing fast; (2) ____ old buildings are being replaced by new skyscrapers. People walk on new concrete sidewalks. The city (3) ____ modern architecture is amazing. There are three new highways and tall bridges over the river.

Many years ago (4) ____ family bought an apartment on Strand Road, next to the river. We could see boats from every room. Now (5) ____ kitchen only has a view of a new skyscraper. When we sit in our living room, we can see (6) ____ favorite movie theater.

1.	a. 's	b. s'	c. its	d. his
2.	a. his	b. 's	c. their	d. its
3.	a. his	b. its	c. 's	d. s'
4.	a. my	b. his	c. 's	d. her
5.	a. our	b. their	c. its	d. s'
6.	a. your	b. s'	c. our	d. its

4 **Read the sentences.** Circle the correct word.

1. The highway **don't** / **doesn't** cross the river.

2. **Do** / **Does** children play in the park?

3. Why **don't** / **doesn't** you like to work in an office?

4. Maya and her daughter **plans** / **plan** a visit to the water tower.

5. **Does** / **Do** we have any clues about the unusual symbols on that wall?

6. Before Coco can go to live **in** / **on** the jungle, she must learn how to climb.

7. Commuting to the city center is more tiring **in** / **on** a bicycle.

8. My cousin's profession is unusual. She tests pet food **in** / **on** a scientist's laboratory!

9. Architects design our sidewalks but they don't think about the people who walk **in** / **on** them.

10. Her brother's friend works **in** / **on** Saudi Arabia as a photographer.

Unit 3
Secrets of the Dark

1 **Read.** Decide whether each sentence describes picture A or B. Write *A* or *B*.

_____ 1. The boy is very active.

_____ 2. The boy is going to sleep.

_____ 3. It's after sunset.

_____ 4. It's daylight.

_____ 5. The street light is lit up.

_____ 6. The street light isn't lit up.

_____ 7. It's dark outside.

_____ 8. It's after sunrise.

2 **Listen.** Then circle the best answers. **TR: 13**

1. Ella walks to school in **darkness** / **daylight**.

2. The students see the **sunrise** / **sunset**.

3. The playground is **lit up** / **not lit up**.

4. When Ella walks home from school, cars drive with **headlights on** / **headlights off**.

5. People in Stockholm **go to sleep** / **are active** when it's dark early.

3 **Read.** Then match the sentence halves about daylight hours in Stockholm. Write the letters.

    In Stockholm, Sweden, there are 18 hours of daylight during the month of June. However, in December, there are only five hours. This causes some health problems. People need the sun's vitamin D for healthy bones and skin. So the residents add extra vitamin D to their winter diet by eating more yogurt and drinking extra milk. Also, they usually take two vacations a year to enjoy the sun.

    There are other problems, too. People feel sad, lose energy, and go out to festivals less often. In the downtown area, tall buildings block the sunlight from reaching the sidewalks, so sometimes offices and homes get less than 5 hours of light a day. However, when it snows, the city looks brighter because streetlights and cars' headlights light up the snow.

_____ 1. In the downtown area, tall buildings

_____ 2. Eating more milk products

_____ 3. Some people feel unhappy

_____ 4. Although Stockholm has very few hours of sunlight in the winter,

_____ 5. One good thing is that when it snows

a. helps people be healthy in the winter months.

b. it has fewer hours of darkness in the summer.

c. the city appears lighter because of the streetlights shining on the snow.

d. when they don't have enough daylight.

e. block the sun, so it's dark.

4 **Write.** Look at the picture and write sentences. Use vocabulary words from the word box.

| active | darkness | streetlights | sunset |

1. _____

2. _____

3. _____

4. _____

GRAMMAR

Present progressive: Saying what is happening now

Non-action verbs	Action verbs
We **understand** your idea.	She**'s wearing** snow boots.
She **doesn't think** it's expensive.	I**'m ice-skating** on the lake.
They **stay** at their grandmother's house in the summer.	You**'re learning** about time zones.
You **look** healthy.	They**'re making** a green glowing light.

Some verbs describe actions: *learn, skate, sing, grow, climb*. We can use the *be + –ing* form with these verbs. *Now we **are learning**. I'm **skating**. They're **singing**.*

Other verbs don't describe actions. We use them to describe situations, feelings, and ideas: *be, live, believe, understand, have, hear, want*. We don't often use the *be + –ing* form with these verbs.

Some non-action verbs can become action verbs with a change in meaning; for example: *think, have*. I **think** this sunset is beautiful. I **am thinking** of the sunset I saw yesterday.

5 **Choose the correct verb to complete each sentence.** Think about if the sentence describes something happening now (*action verb*) or something that is always true (*non-action verb*).

1. She **is wearing** / **wears** a hat and gloves when it is cold at night.

2. He **believes** / **is believing** there's life on Mars.

3. Animals that glow in the dark **include** / **are including** fireflies and jellyfish.

4. David Gruber often **surfs** / **is surfing** when he goes on vacation.

5. Scientists **are learning** / **learn** that more underwater creatures glow in the dark.

6. Kids **love** / **are loving** unusual animals.

7. I'm busy right now. I **am working** / **work** on my report.

6 **Listen.** Circle **A** for *Action* and **NA** for *Non-action*. **TR: 14**

1. **A   NA**   3. **A   NA**   5. **A   NA**   7. **A   NA**   9. **A   NA**
2. **A   NA**   4. **A   NA**   6. **A   NA**   8. **A   NA**   10. **A   NA**

7 **Write.** Put each word under **Day** (sun) or **Night** (moon). Add more words using your own ideas. Then write five sentences using the words from the chart.

| awake   car headlights   dark   darkness   daylight   go to sleep   streetlight   sunset |

Day ☀	Night ☾

1. _____

2. _____

3. _____

4. _____

5. _____

8 **Finish these sentences.** Use vocabulary from this unit. Don't forget to use negatives.

1. During the day a DJ *goes to sleep because he works at night* .

2. We use streetlights, so _____ .

3. In Stockholm, people _____ .

4. At sunset tonight, they _____ .

5. People in many countries use fireworks when _____ .

6. Today, we _____ .

Festival of Lights

Diwali, the Hindu <u>festival</u> of lights, is a fascinating tradition in India. It celebrates the victory of light over darkness and right over wrong. There are some differences in how people observe this festival around the country. In the north, people celebrate the story of a great king's return to his kingdom. In the south, people celebrate it as the day that they fought a great battle. In the west of India, the festival remembers that light returns to Earth, and in the east, people pray for strength. During the festival, there are glowing lights everywhere. People light traditional oil lamps and fireworks.

There are five days of *Diwali*. On the first day, people clean their homes and go shopping for clothes, gold, and kitchen utensils. On the second day, people take a bath before sunrise and then decorate their homes with clay lamps. They also create patterns on the floor using colorful powder or sand. The third day is the most important day of the festival. On that day, families share amazing meals and watch fireworks all night until dawn the next day. The fourth day is the first day of the Hindu New Year. On that day, friends and relatives visit with gifts and best wishes. On the last day, brothers visit their married sisters, who welcome them with a tasty meal.

10 **Read.** Check **T** for *True* or **F** for *False*.

	T	F
1. *Diwali* is a Buddhist festival.	☐	☐
2. Different parts of India celebrate for different reasons.	☐	☐
3. People light fireworks.	☐	☐
4. *Diwali* celebrations go on for four days.	☐	☐
5. People create patterns on the walls of their homes.	☐	☐
6. During the celebration, people visit each other.	☐	☐

11 **Write.** List the activities for the five days of *Diwali* and the reasons people celebrate it in different parts of India.

Day 1: _____

Day 2: _____

Day 3: _____

Day 4: _____

Day 5: _____

North: _____

East: _____

South: _____

West: _____

12 **Write.** How are the *Diwali* festival of lights and the Chinese Lantern Festival similar? Different? Fill in the Venn diagram.

Diwali   **Both**   **Chinese Lantern Festival**

home celebration   bright lights   street celebration

13 **Write.** Imagine you are a writer for your school website blog. Write a few sentences about a local festival you went to.

_____

_____

_____

GRAMMAR

At, *on*, and *in*: Saying when things happen

Our New Year starts **on** January 1.	There's no school **on** Thursday. It's a holiday!
Stockholm has only 5 hours of daylight **in** November.	**In** the evenings, my brother is less active.
During the *Diwali* festival, people take a bath **at** dawn.	The sun rises **at** 9:30 **in** the morning.

We use *on* for days of the week and for specific dates: **on** *Tuesday (morning)*, **on** *June 6*.

We use *in* with months, years, seasons, and periods of time: **in** *February*, **in** *2017*, **in** *(the) winter*, **in** *the morning*, **in** *a minute*.

We use *at* with exact times and certain expressions: **at** *sunset*, **at** *lunchtime*, **at** *3:45 p.m.*

14 **Listen.** Circle *in*, *on*, or *at*. TR: 16

1. Many plants grow (**in** / **on** / **at**) night.

2. The Chinese New Year festival is usually (**in** / **on** / **at**) February.

3. My parents eat lunch (**in** / **on** / **at**) 12:30 p.m.

4. DJs usually work (**in** / **on** / **at**) the weekend.

5. People take a bath (**in** / **on** / **at**) sunrise during the *Diwali* festival.

6. I was born (**in** / **on** / **at**) 2004.

7. These festivals start (**in** / **on** / **at**) the evening.

8. See you (**in** / **on** / **at**) Tuesday morning.

9. Birds are very active (**in** / **on** / **at**) dawn.

10. Don't forget his birthday! It's (**in** / **on** / **at**) April 1, too!

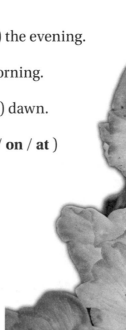

15 **Read Carlos's blog.** Then answer the questions using *at*, *on*, or *in*.

Day 1: Iceland's unique landscape, with its snowy mountains and frozen lakes, is a perfect place for photographers like me. It's mid-winter, and I hear that all over the country you can see the famous Northern Lights, or Aurora Borealis. I'm looking forward to seeing the night sky lit up with green, red, yellow, and purple light. The best view is around midnight, they say. So, here I am! I checked into my hotel. My camera battery is charging, and I'm waiting for the sunset! See you tomorrow!

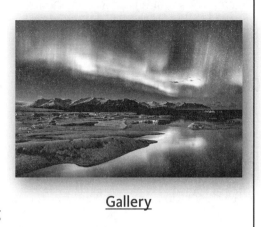
Gallery

1. What time of year are the Northern Lights visible?

_____

2. What time of day or night gives the best view of the Northern Lights?

_____

3. When is the photographer going outdoors to take a photograph?

_____

16 **Read Carlos's blog from Day 2.** Complete the sentences with *at*, *on*, or *in*.

Incredible! I can't believe how beautiful the sky was last night. I left my hotel (1) _at_ 3:30 (2) _____ the afternoon. The sunset was soon after that, (3) _____ around 4:00. The weather here is freezing. It's 23 degrees Fahrenheit (-5 C) (4) _____ sunset. I don't like standing around outside (5) _____ winter, so I decided to go back into the hotel.

(6) _____ about 8:00 (7) _____ the evening, I put on my hat and went outside again. Perfect timing! An amazing green light glowed in the sky in front of me, with lines of purple and red. Wow! More people were outside by now, watching in silence. Click on the gallery link to see my photos. More tomorrow! Flying home (8) _____ Tuesday.

WRITING

We can talk about an event using the five senses as we describe what we see, hear, taste, smell, and feel. With sensory words, our readers imagine that they are there at the event.

17 **Organize**

1. Your topic is to describe a colorful event, for example, a festival, fireworks, a sunset, or watching a wood fire.
2. Plan your writing. Your paragraph should start with an introductory sentence that describes the colorful event. Use the hand below to write three or more sensory words to describe what you see, hear, taste, smell, and feel. If needed, use a dictionary to help.

   Write your introductory sentence here:

   _____

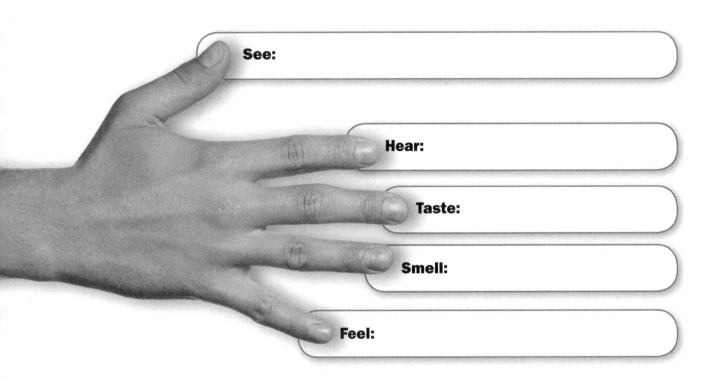

See:

Hear:

Taste:

Smell:

Feel:

3. In your paragraph, use the sensory words you listed to help you describe the colorful event. Finish your paragraph with a brief statement of why this event is special and how you feel about it.

18 **Write**

1. Go to p. 55 in your book. Reread the model and writing prompt.

2. Write your first draft. Check for organization, content, punctuation, capitalization, and spelling.

3. Write your final draft. Share it with your teacher and classmates.

Now I Can . . .

talk about night, darkness, and nocturnal activities.

Choose a nocturnal animal and a light festival. Write two sentences about each.

1. _____

   _____

2. _____

   _____

use non-action and action verbs.

Write two sentences using action verbs and two sentences using non-action verbs.

believe	feel	glow	shine	understand	watch

1. _____

2. _____

3. _____

4. _____

use *at, on,* and *in* to say when things happen.

Write sentences using the following information.

1. morning / watch / sunrise   _____

2. weekend/ ride a bike / park   _____

3. observe / animal / night   _____

write a description of an event using adjectives and the five senses.

Use sensory words to describe your experience at a fireworks show.

_____

_____

_____

Choose an activity. Go to p. 92.

Unit 4
Living Together

1 **Read the clues.** Then complete the words.

1. ____ i ____ ____ l ____ ____ ____   Animals that live in their natural setting

2. ____ ____ ____ f ____ ____ ____ t ____   Fights, disagreements

3. ____ ____ ____ a ____ ____ ____ ____ r   To go away so we can't see something

4. m ____ ____ ____ r ____ ____ ____   To injure, hurt, or be unkind to someone or something

5. ____ c ____ e ____ ____   A way in

6. ____ a ____ ____ t ____ ____   Animals' natural homes

2 **Read.** Complete each sentence with a word from **Activity 1**.

1. At sunset, wild animals come close to the tent, and then they _____ .

2. People who don't take care of their pets _____ them.

3. Amy Dickman studies _____ between wild animals and humans.

4. We had _____ to the mountain area to observe the wild cats.

5. The snow leopard's _____ is in cold, mountainous areas.

6. There's a special relationship between people and _____ .

3 **Listen.** Then check **T** for *True* or **F** for *False*. Rewrite the false sentences to make them true. **TR: 17**

	T	F
1. The program was about animals.	☐	☐
2. He thinks that dogs are wild.	☐	☐
3. She thinks that Siamese crocodiles aren't very smart.	☐	☐
4. The crocodiles' habitat doesn't have any water.	☐	☐
5. We can't live without water.	☐	☐
6. Little animals catch crocodiles.	☐	☐

_____

_____

_____

4 **Read.** Number the sentences in order.

_____ We want to educate the villagers so that they can learn safe ways to live with the wildcats.

_____ To help them, we need to find $2,000 to spend on saving the wildcats in my grandfather's village.

_____ It's called "Save the Wildcats," because we want to help the survival of these animals in Peru.

_____ Good morning, everyone. I want to explain our project to you.

_____ Please give money or your time to help Peru's amazing wildlife live together with local people. Thank you for listening!

_____ People living in the mountains frighten the wildcats away when they use the land for their farms.

Peruvian wildcat

5 **Write.** Complete the notes about the project in Activity 4.

1. In Peru, some villagers are _____.

2. The busy farms _____.

3. At the moment, people don't want to help the cats because_____.

4. This project can help people _____.

5. I think I should _____.

35

GRAMMAR

Modals: Describing obligation and advice

Necessary	We **must help** endangered animals survive. We **have to allow** sea turtles to lay their eggs on our beaches. A conservationist **has to work** in difficult places.
Not necessary	An animal conservationist **doesn't have to be** male. They can be male or female.
Recommended (should/shouldn't)	We **should learn** more about the behavior of unpopular animals, such as rats. People **shouldn't be** afraid of Antiguan racer snakes.

To say that something is necessary, we use the words **_have to_** and **_must_**. They have almost the same meaning, but **_must_** is stronger; there is no other choice. In negative statements, **_don't have to_** shows that something isn't necessary. To give advice, we use **_should_**. Use **_should_** to say it's a good idea, and **_shouldn't_** to say it's not a good idea.

6 **Write.** Use *must, have/has to, don't/doesn't have to,* or *should/shouldn't* according to the clues given in parentheses.

1. Sea turtles are endangered. We _____ protect them. (necessary)

2. People _____ have picnics on beaches where there are sea turtle eggs. (not a good idea)

3. We _____ use plastic bags when we go shopping. (not necessary)

4. We _____ recycle paper. (necessary)

5. People _____ be very careful around mother cats who defend their kittens. (a good idea)

6. You _____ use the car every day. (not necessary)

7. You _____ interact with injured animals. (not a good idea)

8. Animals and people _____ drink water to survive. (necessary)

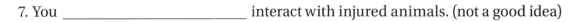

7 **Listen.** Is the idea *necessary, not necessary,* or *recommended*?
Check the correct answer. **TR: 18**

	Necessary	Not necessary	Recommended
1.	☐	☐	☐
2.	☐	☐	☐
3.	☐	☐	☐
4.	☐	☐	☐
5.	☐	☐	☐
6.	☐	☐	☐
7.	☐	☐	☐
8.	☐	☐	☐

8 **Write.** Look at the pictures. Use the clues and *must, has/have to, doesn't/don't have to,* or *should/shouldn't* in your sentences.

1. snake handler / gloves

_____

2. lion / circus

_____

3. bird of prey / fish

_____

4. turtle / plastic bags

_____

9 **Listen and read.** While you read, notice the problems (causes) and the big result (effect).

TR: 19

Stop the boat party—
Lamma Island's sea turtles are in danger!

When you think of Hong Kong, you probably don't think of **wildlife**, right? But one of Hong Kong's islands, Lamma Island, is also home to endangered green sea turtles. Between June and October, they come to the island's Sham Wan beach to lay their eggs.

Special nature police must keep people away from the turtles. At nesting time, you shouldn't go near the beach. If the police see you, you have to pay a fine, which can be a lot of money. However, the police aren't always there to protect the area. The biggest problem is human **behavior**. Boat parties play loud music, and tourists go swimming and have picnics, which **frighten** the turtles away. Scientists and conservationist groups say we **need** a bigger restricted* area to help the turtles **survive**.

Experts agree that green sea turtles in Hong Kong are in danger. The turtles are **disappearing**. One scientist said, "When a turtle is **afraid of** going onto the beach, it has to lay its eggs underwater, where they die." In 2006, there were 14 records of nesting turtles in Sham Wan beach but only two after that, and not a single turtle has been seen since 2012. Another expert said that the number of turtles should increase in the future because now people are working on creating a better **relationship** with the turtles.

*restricted *adj.* with limits, closed-off

10 **Read the text again.** Find four problems (causes) that contribute to a result (effect) for the green sea turtles.

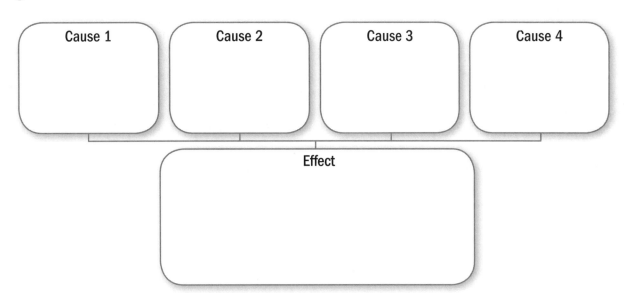

| Cause 1 | Cause 2 | Cause 3 | Cause 4 |

Effect

11 **Summarize the text.** Tell someone about the Hong Kong green sea turtles. Write sentences about the problems, the result, and a possible solution.

1. One problem for the turtles is that _____.

2. Another problem for the turtles is _____.

3. A third problem for the turtles is _____.

4. Conservationists think _____.

5. One solution is _____.

12 **Write.** Think about the information from the texts in this unit. You have read about different problems between humans and animals. Complete the list of advice.

At home: We _____.

At the beach: People _____.

In the mountains: Villagers _____.

GRAMMAR

Modals: Describing ability in present and past

Crocodiles **can sleep** with one eye open.	At that time, turtles **could lay** their eggs on the beaches.
Most domestic animals **can't survive** in the wild.	Conservation groups **couldn't rescue** all the birds.
Why **can't** we **interact** with wildlife easily in a city?	The injured deer **couldn't avoid** the predators.

We use *can/can't* to talk about ability in the present. We use *could/couldn't* to talk about ability in the past.

13 **Listen.** Circle the word you hear. TR: 20

1. The baby panda **can / can't** see people.

2. They **could / couldn't** understand animals before.

3. Trained dogs **can / can't** sniff for chemicals.

4. They **can / can't** drive to the injured snow leopard.

5. They **could / couldn't** save all the birds.

6. We **can / can't** avoid using plastic bags.

7. The turtles **could / couldn't** lay their eggs.

14 **Read.** Underline the phrases with *can*, *can't*, *could*, or *couldn't*. Then circle the correct word to complete the sentence.

The Survival of the Antiguan Racer Snake

The Antiguan racer is probably the world's least known snake. It's not dangerous and it can't kill you. However, these snakes are slowly disappearing from Bird Island, a small island off the coast of Antigua. How can we save these racers?

Conservationist Jenny Daltry studies the snakes, so we can now understand the Antiguan racers' habitat and behavior. During her five-year project, they have removed the racers' biggest predators, black rats, from the island. Now the rats can't prey on the snakes' eggs. However, the snakes can still die because of hurricanes or bad weather conditions, other predators, and tourists.

Sadly, there's also another problem. Bird Island is so small that only about 100 racer snakes could survive there. Jenny's team hopes that they can introduce racers to other nearby islands. They have already saved the Antiguan racer; we can be sure that, without this project, this snake would disappear.

You can read about Jenny's project in an article on the Internet.

Because of this project, more racer snakes **can** / **can't** survive on Bird Island.

15 **Read the article again.** Complete these sentences using *can*, *can't*, *could*, or *couldn't*.

1. The Antiguan racer snakes _____.

2. Black rats _____.

3. Jenny and her team _____.

4. The five-year project _____.

5. Hurricanes, predators, and tourists _____.

6. Researchers hope that _____.

7. This project means that now people _____.

8. You _____ on the Internet.

WRITING

After you write, you need to read your work and check it. Ask yourself some questions: Is my writing organized? Are the ideas clear? Circle any spelling and grammar mistakes. Finally, rewrite your work and proofread it for any last changes.

16 Organize

1. Your topic is a relationship between a person and an animal. Think of a relationship you know, have read about, or seen in a movie. How would you describe the relationship? Make a list of your ideas in the chart.

Person	Animal

2. Plan your writing. You'll need an introductory paragraph with a topic sentence. Your topic sentence will state the relationship between the person and the animal. Write your topic sentence here:

_____

Next, you'll need a paragraph to describe the relationship and how the person and animal interact. Explain the situation with a few details.

Remember to finish your paragraph with a brief statement of why this relationship is special.

17 Write

1. Go to p. 37 in your book. Reread the model and writing prompt.

2. Write your first draft. Check for organization, content, punctuation, capitalization, and spelling.

3. Write your final draft. Share it with your teacher and classmates.

Now I Can . . .

talk about interactions between animals and humans.

☐ Yes, I can!
☐ I think I can.
☐ I need more practice.

Describe the relationship of the man and the baby elephant.
Write two or three sentences.

_____

_____

_____

use modals to describe obligation and advice.

☐ Yes, I can!
☐ I think I can.
☐ I need more practice.

Complete the sentences according to the clues. Use *must, has/have to,*
doesn't/don't have to, or *should/shouldn't.*

1. I _____ help this injured animal, so it can survive.
   (very necessary)

2. Animals have feelings, too. You _____ mistreat them. (advice)

3. We _____ keep the seas free of plastic bags. (necessary)

use modals to describe ability in the present and past.

☐ Yes, I can!
☐ I think I can.
☐ I need more practice.

Complete the sentences with *can/could* or *can't/couldn't.*

1. A mountain lion _____ climb over a 12-foot wall.

2. When it was born, the baby panda's eyes were closed. It _____ see.

3. Yesterday, they _____ rescue some sea turtles.

**write a description of a special relationship between an animal
and a human.**

☐ Yes, I can!
☐ I think I can.
☐ I need more practice.

Describe a situation in which an animal interacts with a human.

_____

_____

_____

Choose an activity. Go to p. 93.

Units 3–4 Review

1 **Read.** Then choose the correct words.

A
Please don't call me today.
I'm not feeling very well and
(1) **I'm staying / I stay** in bed.
Call me (2) **on/ at** about 10:00
tomorrow morning. I (3) **want /
am wanting** to check our science
project before class (4) **on / at**
Monday.

B
After our meeting today, I had another idea.
I can't (1) **go to sleep / asleep** without telling
you. I think we can ask teachers to talk to kids
about how important it is to (2) **interact /
rescue** with wildlife and learn about the
animals' behavior and habitat. We can write a
letter (3) **in / at** the morning to local schools.
What do you think?

C
Are you (1) **observe / observing** wildlife? Don't forget
to take photographs of the birds, mice, rabbits, and
insects around your home (2) **on / in** the weekend! Get
up early both days, (3) **on / at** sunrise. Bring your photos to Monday's club meeting (4) **at /on** 1 p.m.

2 **Listen.** Then choose the best answer. **TR: 21**

1. Cars _____ .

   a. stop to rescue salamanders
   b. kill salamanders in the darkness
   c. with headlights help salamanders

2. The speakers agree that _____ .

   a. salamanders are very clever
   b. salamanders are afraid of cars
   c. salamanders should move faster

3. Snakes _____ .

   a. hunt salamanders
   b. don't hunt salamanders
   c. eat insects

3 **Read.** Choose the best answer for each blank.

   A conservation magazine reports that we must try to (1) _____ the destruction of our planet. When people cut down trees to construct new buildings, they are destroying animals' (2) _____ . Forests are homes to thousands of (3) _____ animals. Now these animals (4) _____ find new places to live. Some animals go into towns and villages because they can't (5) _____ for food in the forests. It (6) _____ dangerous in North Canada, for example. While people are (7) _____ , wild bears have easy access to waste food in trash cans. Our relationship with animals (8) _____ change if we want to share our planet.

1. **a.** avoid   **b.** keep   **c.** not
2. **a.** horizon   **b.** time zones   **c.** habitats
3. **a.** tame   **b.** wild   **c.** smart
4. **a.** have to   **b.** need   **c.** should
5. **a.** observe   **b.** defend   **c.** hunt
6. **a.** is becoming   **b.** are becoming   **c.** should becoming
7. **a.** asleep   **b.** awake   **c.** injured
8. **a.** couldn't   **b.** shouldn't   **c.** must

4 **Read the sentences.** Use the words in the box to complete the second sentence so that the meaning is the same as the first sentence. Use no more than one word for each blank.

| at | couldn't | observe | mistreat | predator | relationship | sunrise | sunset |

1. While people are asleep, wild bears hunt for food in North Canada. Wild bears sniff around the trash cans in North Canada _____*at*_____ night.

2. When it's 7 a.m. in Europe, it's 12:30 p.m. in India. When I see the _____ here in Spain, my friend in India is finishing her lunch!

3. I think the sky is more beautiful when the sun goes down. I believe _____ is more beautiful.

4. The world of insects fascinates me. I love to _____ ants, spiders, and tiny animals.

5. People interact with domestic animals. Pets, such as cats and dogs, are easy to have a _____ with.

6. Snakes eat mice and salamanders. Salamanders and mice have the same _____ —snakes.

7. Reports say that aquatic parks treat dolphins and whales very well. I hope that aquatic parks don't _____ their sea creatures.

8. Yesterday the rats were not able to sniff any of the landmines. The rats _____ find any landmines yesterday.

Unit 5
What We Wear

1 **Organize the clothes.** Decide if the clothes are practical, formal, or casual.
Write P, F or C.

2 **Write.** Put words that describe the images in Activity 1 into the puzzle. Then answer the question.

business suit	denim jacket	firefighter's uniform	high heels	jeans
pants	shirt	sneakers	sweatshirt	tie

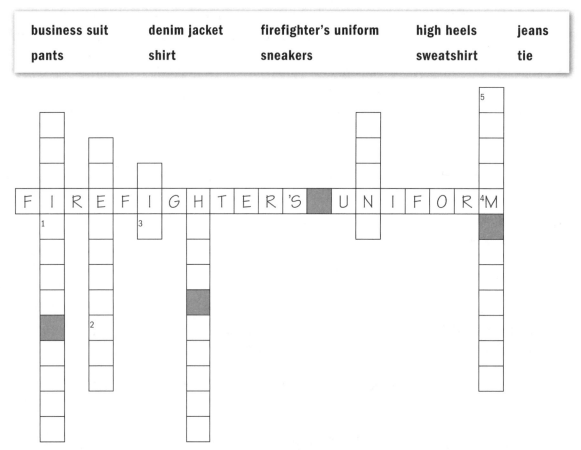

Write the letters from the numbered boxes. Then unscramble the letters to find which
nineteenth-century practical fabric is now a twenty-first-century fashion fabric.

1	2	3	4	5

3 **Listen.** Complete the student's survey. Then write your answers in the last row. TR: 22

Interviewees	What are you wearing today?	What do you wear on the weekend?
Martin		
Mrs. Gardener		
Fiona		
You		

4 **Draw.** Listen to TR: 22 again. Draw the clothes in your notebook. Talk about them in class.

5 **Write.** Survey your friends and classmates. Use words from this unit and your own questions.

Example questions: Do you like to dress up for a party? Which formal clothes do you wear?

casual	denim	dress up	formal	heels	jeans
practical	suit	sweatshirt	tie	tights	uniform

Interviewees		

GRAMMAR

Simple past: Saying what happened

Ami photograph**ed** people in Kenya and India.
They dress**ed** up for the wedding party.
He **didn't dress up** for school.
They **didn't wear** high heels.

Questions:
Did the women paint their hands?
Why **did** they tattoo their faces?

Verbs change when we talk about past events. Most verbs add -*ed* (protect → protect**ed**)

Be careful with spelling! Verbs ending in *e* add -*d* (love → love**d**)

Some verbs double the final letter, then add -*ed* (stop → sto**pped**)

---

6 **Read.** These facts are about the tattoos of Maoris from New Zealand and the Chin people from Myanmar. Are the facts the same (**S**) or different (**D**)? Write **S** or **D**. Then complete the sentences about the Maori and Chin people.

_____ 1. Maori men and women decorated their faces with tattoos. Chin women painted tattoos on their faces.

_____ 2. Maoris used tattoos to show people from other villages or tribes where they lived. Chin women's tattoos showed their village group or tribe.

_____ 3. The government stopped the Chin people putting tattoos on their faces. Maori people didn't stop using tattoos because of the government.

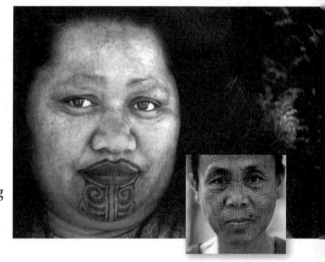

1. In the past, Chin and Maori people both _____

2. Before, Chin women _____

3. The New Zealand government _____

48

7 **Listen.** Draw an arrow. Is the action now or in the past? **TR: 23**

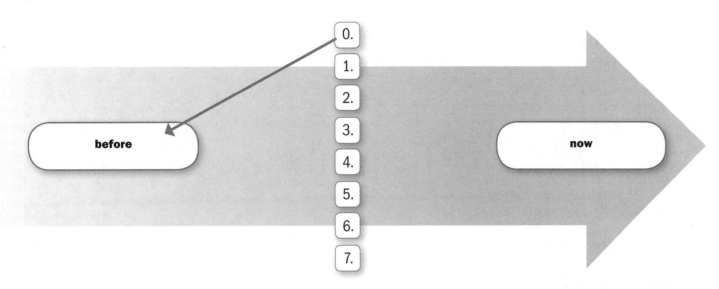

0.
1.
2.
3.
4.
5.
6.
7.

before

now

8 **Write.** Change the verbs into the past tense to complete the sentences.

1. In the past, Indian mothers (decorate) _____ their daughters' hands and feet.

2. Most Indian brides (pierce) _____ their noses with expensive jewelry.

3. Five thousand years ago, brides (dress up) _____ in bright colors on their wedding days, and this continues today.

4. In the past, many Indian women (collect) _____ over 50 bracelets on one arm, but now they don't wear so many.

5. In the past, Indian men (save) _____ jewelry, but now they save money in the bank.

9 **Write.** Use the words below to write sentences about what people liked to wear in the past. Change the verbs; include some negative verbs. Write one sentence below. Then write four more in your notebooks.

gold jewelry	hair
hazmat suit	high heels
jade bracelets	patterns	tattoos

believe	collect	decorate
like	protect	pull
save	tattoo	use

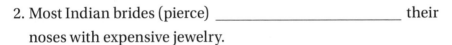

Many centuries ago, men in India didn't save money in banks. However, they collected gold jewelry.

_____

10 **Listen and read.** While you read the article, notice the events in the past and the events in the present. Answer the questions. **TR: 24**

the History of Jeans

¹ In 1873 two Americans discovered that a cotton fabric called "jeane" was very strong and practical for outdoor work. Because the fabric came from Nimes (*de Nimes* in French), they called the fabric *denim*. It all started when a customer asked a tailor named Jacob W. Davis to make some strong pants for her husband. Davis bought some denim from Levi Strauss's shop, and he added rivets to make the pockets strong. The happy husband showed his friends.

pocket

rivet

² Davis and Strauss quickly sold 200 more pairs of jeans, but they didn't want other people to copy their idea. So they registered their new product with the government right away, and May 20, 1873, became the birthday of blue jeans.

³ Today there are many products made of denim, such as bags, boots, and ties. Even jewelry such as bracelets, necklaces, and hair decorations can be made from denim. Some designers re-use old jeans to create new fashion products, too.

⁴ In the 1800s, or just over a century ago, denim was almost a uniform for outdoor workers. Most people wore it. Today you can spend a lot of money on a denim designer outfit or show your wealth by wearing a diamond accessory on your jeans pocket. But if you don't have $1,000 to spare, you can still dress up in jeans by wearing high heels.

⁵ Look around you. How many people do you see wearing jeans? There must be a good reason! Maybe it's because jeans are made of a very practical fabric.

1. What did the customer ask the tailor Jacob W. Davis to make? _____

2. How many pairs of pants did David and Strauss sell quickly? _____

3. Name three products made of denim. _____

4. What accessory can you wear on the pocket of your jeans? _____

5. What does the writer believe is the reason for the success of jeans?

_____

11 **Read again.** Find verbs in the simple past tense. Write the events they describe under **In the past**. Write present-day actions in the **Now** column.

In the past	Now

12 **Read the summary.** Write the words from the box in the spaces. Practice telling a classmate or teacher about the history of jeans.

added	denim	fabric	jeans	practical	wanted

"Jeane" was a strong, cotton (1) _____ sold in America 200 years ago.

A woman (2) _____ new pants for her husband.

Jacob Davis bought some (3) _____ from Levi Strauss.

He (4) _____ rivets to make the pockets strong.

Many workers liked the jeans because they were (5) _____ .

Davis and Strauss registered their new pants in 1873 so that nobody could copy their (6) _____ .

13 **Read again.** You have read about the history of football uniforms and jeans. Make new sentences about how your clothes have changed over time. Use simple past tense verbs.

_____

_____

_____

_____

GRAMMAR

Simple past: Describing what happened

You **were** in the clothes shop.	She **kept** extra tights in her bag.
I **was** in the shoe shop.	We **left** our jackets at the door.
He **had** a denim jacket in his hand.	He **got** a tie as a birthday present.
They **put** their cell phones in their pockets.	Shops **sold** thousands of pairs of jeans.
I **began** jewelry classes last year.	I **brought** your sweatshirt for you.

Questions

To form questions with be:

Were you in the clothes shop this morning? **Was** she in the shoe shop?

All other verbs begin with did / didn't:

Didn't you **see** the fashion show? **Did** they **do** exercises to keep healthy?

Some verbs in the simple past do not add *-ed*. They are irregular verbs: *be, begin, bring, buy, do, eat, get, give, have, keep, leave, make, mean, put, see, sell, think, wear*. These past-tense verbs are used often. We must memorize them!

These verbs don't change forms in the simple past: *I (you/he/she/it/we/you/they)* **wore** *new shoes.*

The verb *be* changes when used in the simple past: *I* **was** *(you* **were**, *he/she/it* **was**, *we/you/they* **were**) *in the shoe shop.*

14 **Write.** Look at the photos. Write the verbs in the middle column to complete the sentences.

became	bought	meant	sold	was	were	wore

Ski fashion		different in the past.
The clothes		thick and loose.
People		wool and cotton pants and jackets.
In the 1970s new fabric		available.
Shops		light-weight jackets.
Advanced technology		that fabric changed.
Skiers		colorful all-in-one suits.

15 **Listen.** Circle the correct simple past verb. **TR: 25**

1. **thought** / **bought**   4. **got** / **put**

2. **was** / **had**   5. **sold** / **got**

3. **was** / **were**   6. **gave** / **had**

16 **Read the interview.** Write similar questions to interview an older person you know. Show your survey questions in class. If possible, ask your interview questions.

Interviewer:	*Good morning, Mr. Daniels. Thank you for speaking to us today.*
Mr. Daniels:	*No problem. How can I help?*
Interviewer:	*Could you tell us about how school clothes were different when you were a boy?*
Mr. Daniels:	*Oh, well, in my school the uniform was very formal. We wore short, heavy wool pants. I had a hat and tie too.*

Question When did you buy your first pair of jeans?

Answer _____

Question _____

Answer _____

Question _____

Answer _____

Question _____

Answer _____

Question _____

Answer _____

WRITING

The last stage in writing is publishing. When you publish your work, you let other people read it. But first, you need to make sure it is as good as it can be. You know how to write, review and proofread your work. Do one last check before you show a classmate or teacher.

17 **Organize**

1. Your topic is to write an essay about a uniform that has changed over time. Think about different types of uniforms, how they are used now, and how they were used in the past. Decide on one type of uniform to research. List changes in clothes, styles, materials, and decorations.

2. Plan your ideas. Decide who your readers are. Decide where to publish your paragraph.

Uniform	
Before	
Now	
My readers	
Place for publishing	
Topic sentence	

18 **Write**

1. Go to p. 89 in your book. Reread the history of soccer uniforms.

2. In your notebook, write the first draft of your paragraph about how a uniform has changed over time. Proofread your work. Check your simple past verbs.

3. Write your final draft. Check one last time, and publish it for your readers.

Now I Can . . .

talk about fashion changes through history.

Write about how some clothes have changed over time. Write four sentences.

1. In the past, _____

2. Now, _____

3. In the past, _____

4. Now, _____

use regular simple past verbs.

Write sentences using the past tense of some of these words.

attach	color	decorate	dress up	look	mix	pierce	prefer	protect	use

1. _____

2. _____

3. _____

use irregular simple past verbs.

Choose words from the box to write sentences using the past tense.

begin	bring	buy	eat	get	give	keep	leave	put	see	sell	think

1. _____

2. _____

3. _____

write and share my description of clothes that changed over time.

Write two sentences about your personal fashion changes. Share your description with a classmate or teacher.

_____

_____

Choose an activity. Go to p. 94.

Unit 6
Mix and Mash

1 **Find the new vocabulary words.** Look again at pages 94–96 in your book. Find a word that begins with each letter. X = no word.

A _____ B bands C _____ D _____

　　　　E _____ F _____ G Gokh-Bi

H _____ I _____ J Japanese K -X- L -X-

M _____ N no O _____ P _____

Q -X- R _____ S _____ T _____

　　　U urban V _____ W West Africa

　　　　　X -X- Y you Z -X-

2 **Write.** Cross out the word that doesn't connect to the people. Then choose from the remaining words to complete the sentences. Circle the letter—is it picture A, B, or C?

A. DJ
electronic, mix,
song, traditional

B. Band
electronic, traditional,
hit, perform

C. Filmmaker
download, edit,
recording, video

1. This DJ can _____ two songs together to make a new electronic
   sound. **A B C**

2. This person works in cities. Her urban _____ stories are
   cool! **A B C**

3. This is a _____ band. They use natural materials to make their
   instruments. **A B C**

3 **Listen.** Answer the questions. **TR: 26**

1. What type of radio show is it? _____

2. The DJ asks three questions. Put them in order. Write 1, 2 and 3.

    a. Whose DJ mix wins the top position? _____

    b. What is the top hit this week? _____

    c. Which song did listeners choose as the top recording? _____

3. Who does the DJ interview? _____

4. Why does he interview her? _____

5. How did she start her music career? _____

6. Do you like electronic music? Why or why not? _____

_____

4 **Draw and write.** Complete the storyboard for a video. Look at the beginning and then draw your ideas for the middle and the end. Use words from the word bank. Tell a classmate about your video.

edit	electronic	fan	hit
hybrid	imitate	include	mix
more	newer	original	perform
popular	record	song	traditional

This traditional band imitates sounds from the forests in Gabon.		

GRAMMAR

Adjectives: Comparing two or more things

The band didn't perform their **older** hits.	It's **more difficult** to buy tickets this year.
The light show was **as cool as** last year.	Modern dance is **less tiring than** traditional dance.
The fans are **noisier** tonight than last week!	In my opinion, CDs are **better than** downloads.
The song from the movie *Spectre* was a **bigger** hit than other Bond movie songs.	The sound quality is **worse** with downloads.

We use comparatives to compare two things. Use *more* before adjectives that have two or more syllables. Add *-er* to adjectives that have just one syllable. With two-syllable adjectives that end in *y*, both options are possible (***more*** noisy or noisi**er**). Remember to change *y* to *i* before adding *-er*.

Some adjectives have irregular comparative forms: *good* → **better**; *bad* → **worse**

We use *as . . . as . . .* to describe how things are similar or the same.

5 **Complete the conversation.** Think of the opposites of the words in bold and compare the two things.

Gustav: These new hybrid sports are not **bad**. What do you think? I know you can't play many sports, so which one is (1) _____better_____ for you?

Katia: Disc golf isn't **difficult**, is it? I think it's a little (2) _____ than traditional golf. Do you agree?

Gustav: Sure. It uses **soft** plastic discs, not balls. Those plastic discs are not as (3) _____ as golf balls when you make a mistake!

Katia: Also there aren't any **heavy** golf clubs. Discs are (4) _____ .

Gustav: That's true. And disc golf is **cheap**. My parents say that their golf membership is (5) _____ every year!

Katia: But isn't golf **boring**? Let's try something (6) _____ ! What do you think of volcano boarding?

6 Read. Find the differences in the musician's notes about two recordings. Change the words in the box to finish the sentences.

Version 1: 11/12/2016
Track 1: Drums – volume high
Bass guitar comes in too late.
Piano OK – but slow in the middle.
Guitar – OK

Version 2: 11/17/2016
Track 1: Drums – volume low
Bass guitar – much better now.
Piano – love it!
Guitar – can't hear it!

| early | fast | loud | old | quiet |

1. Version 1, from November 12, is _____ than Version 2.

2. The drums on Version 1 are _____ than the drums on Version 2.

3. In Version 2 the bass guitar comes in _____ than in Version 1.

4. The piano is _____ in the middle of Version 2.

5. In Version 2 the guitar is _____ .

7 Listen. Which picture is the speaker describing, in your opinion? Circle A or B. Then complete the sentences. TR: 27

A

B

1. I love these hybrid lamps! Lamp A / B is (cool) _____ than lamp A / B
because _____ .

2. I think lamp A / B is (useful) _____ than lamp A / B because
_____ .

3. Which version is good? Lamp A / B is (good/bad) _____ than lamp

A / B because _____ .

4. Lamp A / B is (bright) _____ than lamp A / B because

_____ .

8 **Listen and read.** While you read, notice the differences between the traditional and the modern activities. **TR: 28**

Jumping Rope Filipino Style

1. Mix the past with the present and you get a traditional dance from the Philippines plus a cool new type of sports activity! Tinikling is a fun form of exercise that combines rhythm with fast foot- and legwork. The original sport began in central Philippines and imitates the tikling bird walking carefully through grass and bamboo. Tinikling improves awareness of space and includes skills similar to jumping rope. Every year young people perform it in school shows all over the Philippines, and audiences love it.

2. Tinikling is a type of dance that involves two people hitting bamboo poles together and on the ground. This makes the beat or rhythm. At the same time, one or more dancers step over and in between the poles. It's not easy, especially for girls who wear long traditional dresses! In the traditional dance, bamboo poles make the beat along with music from a type of string instrument. Today's twenty-first century version uses simpler, four-beat electronic dance music.

3. There are many tinikling products available now, such as tinikling songs on CDs and audio downloads, dance-step instruction videos, and tinikling sticks made of bamboo or plastic. For the traditional version, you must find thick bamboo poles, but be careful—just imagine the pain if you make a mistake!

9 **Read the article again.** Answer the questions.

1. What activity is tinikling similar to?

_____

2. What are the dancers and the bamboo poles imitating?

_____

3. What modern-day products can we buy for tinikling?

_____

10 **Reread the article.** Compare the differences and similarities between the traditional dance and the sport of today. Practice telling a classmate or your teacher about tinikling.

Tinikling traditional dance   **Both**   **Today's sport**

11 **Write.** Read the text again. Write two new sentences about changes in this traditional dance.

Example: The traditional music for the dance was more complex than today's four-beat rhythm.

_____

_____

_____

_____

GRAMMAR

Count and noncount nouns: Talking about amounts

Count nouns	Noncount nouns
Many / Some / A lot of / A few cultures have a traditional dance. They perform **a few** traditional songs. She saw **a couple of** shows last month.	**Some / A little / A lot of** / modern dance mixes words too. Listening to **a little** music before the show is a good idea. There is **too much** information on fan websites.
Questions How **many** downloads were there? Were there **many** fans outside the door?	**Questions** How **much** money do we need? Did they make **much** noise?

Count nouns are nouns we can count (*one song, two songs*). Noncount nouns are nouns we can't count (*music, time*). They don't have a plural form. We can't use *a / an* or numbers before noncount nouns. Use *a few / many* to talk about count nouns and *a little / much* to talk about noncount nouns.

12 **Read.** Look at the nouns in **bold** and circle *NC* (noncount nouns) or *C* (count nouns).

1. Hiro is planning his birthday meal, so he's checking how much **food** he has ready. (NC / C)

2. Is there enough **soda**? (NC / C)

3. Hiro needs to buy two or three more **bottles** of soda. (NC / C)

4. He wants to share a birthday **pizza**. A sushi-pizza! (NC / C)

5. Eight people need some **pizza**. (NC / C)

6. Everyone will probably eat at least one **piece** of sushi-pizza. (NC / C)

7. Hiro only bought two **boxes** of sushi-pizza. (NC / C)

8. His friends all love sushi-pizza. Hiro has to buy more **pizza**. (NC / C)

13 **Write.** Look at this menu. Sort the food in **bold** into count and noncount nouns.

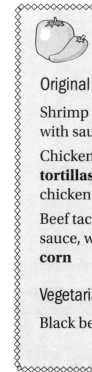

Viva Tacos! Traditional Mexican flour and corn tortillas

Original Classic **tacos**

Shrimp taco: Two fresh, grilled **shrimp** with sauce and lime **juice** in a soft tortilla

Chicken tacos: Two medium, soft, corn **tortillas**, wrapped around **slices** of chicken

Beef taco: Ground **beef** in a thick tomato sauce, wrapped in a soft tortilla made of **corn**

Vegetarian **dishes**

Black bean or roast vegetable tacos

Salad

Black **rice** salad, green salad, tomato salad, green tomato salad

Salsa

Cheese **sauce**, spicy tomato sauce, lemon **mayonnaise**, spicy green sauce

American fast-food style

Fried tortillas: Replace the soft tortilla with a USA crispy version.

Nachos: Fried corn **chips** with your choice of salsa

Count nouns	Noncount nouns

14 **Listen.** What do the friends choose to eat? **TR: 29**

Choice 1: _____

Choice 2: _____

Choice 3: _____

15 **Write.** Read the menu again. Write questions about some of the food in the box.

black rice	**chicken slices**	**lemon mayonnaise**
roast vegetable tacos	**spicy tomato sauce**	**corn tortillas**

How many: _____

How much: _____

Are there: _____

Is there: _____

WRITING

A good paragraph of exemplification introduces your idea and uses examples to support that idea. We use *for example*, *another example*, and *such as* to introduce these supporting sentences.

16 Organize

1. Your topic is to write a paragraph about your own unique ani-mix. Think of two or more animals and mix them together. Draw your animal in your notebook. You need to imagine its name and write examples of how it is unique.

2. Plan your ideas in the chart. Research your chosen animals, their appearance and what they can do. If possible, create a photo of your chosen ani-mix to go with your paragraph.

	Animal 1	Animal 2	Animal 3
Name			
Size and appearance			
Body parts (legs, wings)			
Abilities (climbs, swims)			

17 Write

1. Go to p. 105 in your book. Reread the model and writing prompt.

2. Write your first draft. Check for organization, content, punctuation, capitalization, and spelling.

3. Write your final draft. Share it with your teacher and classmates.

Now I Can . . .

talk about how two things combine to make something new.

Write three sentences about how artists combine ideas.

□ Yes, I can!
□ I think I can.
□ I need more practice.

1. _____

2. _____

3. _____

compare two or more things.

Complete the sentences using the given words.

□ Yes, I can!
□ I think I can.
□ I need more practice.

1. Tinikling is _____ (cool) than jumping rope.

2. Mash-up music is _____ (difficult) to perform than many people think.

3. I think cooking fried rice is _____ (easy) than baking cakes.

use count and noncount nouns.

Write sentences using these words.

| food | meat | songs | videos |

□ Yes, I can!
□ I think I can.
□ I need more practice.

1. _____

2. _____

3. _____

4. _____

write a paragraph of exemplification.

Write about your idea for a new mix of art, sports, or music. Support your idea with examples. Plan and check your paragraph. Present it to your classmates and teacher.

□ Yes, I can!
□ I think I can.
□ I need more practice.

_____

_____

_____

Choose an activity. Go to p. 95.

Units 5–6 Review

1 **Read.** Choose the correct word to complete the sentences.

1. Wei doesn't like formal clothes.

   He takes off his school _____ as soon as he gets home.
   a. uniform **b.** jeans **c.** tights

2. The DJ preferred the second version of the song.

   He thought the newer mix was _____ than the first one.
   a. worse **b.** better **c.** noisier

3. I like to include stars in all my paintings.

   I _____ stars into all my art work.
   a. mix **b.** perform **c.** record

4. What type of _____ was the singer wearing on her arms and wrists?
   a. necklace **b.** tie **c.** bracelet

5. My mother works in a laboratory.

   She has to wear a special suit for _____ reasons.
   a. practical **b.** formal **c.** casual

6. Video game designers have to be more creative every year. They have to

   _____ cool, new ideas that nobody has tried.
   a. combine **b.** imitate **c.** imagine

2 **Listen.** Decide if the sentence is *True* (T) or *False* (F). **TR: 30**

1. The original recording was from the 1980s. _____

2. He doesn't like formal clothes. _____

3. She thinks her friend looks good. _____

4. The girl asks for her mother's opinion about her hair. _____

5. The boy prefers traditional guitar music. _____

3 **Read.** Choose the best answer to the questions.

1.   The wimple was a popular head covering for women in Europe from the twelfth through the fifteenth centuries. Wimples were usually made of cotton or silk. They provided protection from the weather, and they were a way to dress up for formal occasions. Sometimes the wimple covered the top of the head and shoulders and went around the neck, finishing up at the chin.

2.   Wealthy women sometimes used the wimple to display their jewelry. They decorated the cloth before placing it on their head. Sometimes a circle of fabric or metal, like a queen's crown, was placed on the head to hold the wimple in place.

3.   Head covering is an ancient fashion for both women and men. Many centuries ago, men and women in Ancient Greece, Rome, and China covered their heads for a variety of reasons. Today people from countries around the Mediterranean still wear similar coverings to protect them from the strong sun and to dress up on formal occasions.

1. What was the wimple made from?
   a. wool   **b.** denim   **c.** cotton

2. For how many centuries was the wimple in fashion in Europe?
   a. six   **b.** four   **c.** one

3. Which part of the body did the wimple not cover?
   a. shoulders   **b.** hands   **c.** neck

4. What did some women add to their wimple to show their wealth?
   a. jewelry   **b.** paint   **c.** flowers

4 **Read the sentences.** Circle the correct word.

1. My sweatshirt looks cleaner than yours because I **wash / washed** it last week.

2. **Some / Much** brides in Morocco still **paint / painted** their hands, and in this way they keep the tradition alive.

3. **Many / Much** Indian women **pierce / pierced** their noses when they got married.

4. Today **a few / a little** young Maoris still **wear / wore** tattoos on their faces.

5. When she was a teenager, my mom **loves / loved** hybrid songs.

6. Last year my neighbor **hates / hated** my favorite type of music, but now she likes **much / many** of it!

Unit 7
Cool Apps and Gadgets

1 **Write.** Find four vocabulary words or phrases from this unit on the screen. Then use them to complete the text message.

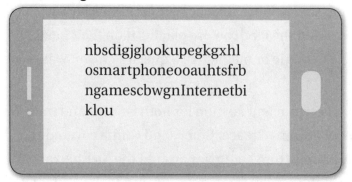

nbsdigjglookupegkgxhl
osmartphoneooauhtsfrb
ngamescbwgnInternetbi
klou

Can you please _____

2 **Write.** Use words from the word bank to send a message. Write on the smartphone.

apps	chat	connect	incredible	mobile	possible	search
send	share	tablet	text	useful	Wi-Fi	

3 **Read.** Match the words with the definitions. Write the letter on the line.

_____ 1. chat   a. to allow another person to use something too

_____ 2. share   b. able to move from place to place

_____ 3. mobile   c. to join two things together

_____ 4. connect   d. about computer technology

_____ 5. digital   e. to talk

4 **Listen.** Match each speaker to his or her words. Write the name on the line. **TR: 31**

1. _____

> I love using mobile apps to chat with my friends.

2. _____

> It's easier to send a text than to walk upstairs to my room, says my mom!

3. _____

> Sorry, I need help with my photo-sharing app.

4. _____

> Share my gadget webpage!

5 **Complete the responses.** Use words from the box and your own ideas.

gadgets	Internet	look up	share	smartphone	useful

1. I'll send everybody the coolest photo from the party—this is my favorite!

   Please don't _____

2. I'll send a text when I get on the train. It's the easiest way to talk to you.

   Did you _____

3. My brother's going to ask for a tablet as a birthday present. He needs to search the Internet and wants to play games, but a basic version is OK.

   Lucky him! For my next birthday, _____

4. Are you going to finish your electricity project before Friday? I'm not! Can you please send me some useful images?

   We need to search for _____

GRAMMAR

Superlatives: Talking about extremes

The scariest part of the movie is at the beginning.
This dictionary app is **the most useful** one I have.
This game scores **the highest** in this year's reviews, but it's my least favorite.
That café on the corner has **the worst** Wi-Fi connection in town.

We use superlatives to compare one thing in a group to the rest of the group. Superlatives always take *the*.

Use *most* before adjectives that have two or more syllables:

It's **the most difficult** computer game.

Add *–est* to adjectives that have just one syllable:

This is **the loudest** setting on my mobile phone.

With two-syllable adjectives that end in *y*, both options are possible: *the scariest* or *the most scary*. (Remember to change *y* to *i*.)

Use *least* with any adjective: *the **least** difficult, the **least** scary, the **least** loud.*

Some adjectives have their own superlative form: *good/bad* → **the best**/**the worst**.

6 **Read.** Circle the correct words. Complete the reviews.

1. This **keyboard / camera / battery** is for French speakers.
   It's (+/unusual) _____ one I've ever seen.

2. When we watch videos on our smartphones, we use a lot of **battery / camera / keyboard**
   life. (+/good) _____ one lasts one whole day.

3. The **microphone / camera / keyboard** on this video camera is not (+/powerful)
   _____ , but it's built-in, so it's easier to transport and you never forget it.

4. We all know that the **keyboard / screen / battery** on a smartphone is easy to break. Today
   I dropped (+/ expensive) _____ phone I've ever had and broke it!

7 **Listen.** While you listen, read the questions. Listen again and circle the letters. **TR: 32**

1. Which camera is the least expensive?	A	B	C	D
2. Which camera has the smallest screen?	A	B	C	D
3. Which product has the worst zoom?	A	B	C	D
4. Which is the heaviest?	A	B	C	D
5. Which is the most expensive to buy?	A	B	C	D

8 **Write.** Match the opposites. Then change the pairs to their superlatives. Choose one word from the pair to complete the statements.

| easy | good | high | loud |

| bad | difficult | low | quiet |

_____ *easiest* _____   _____ *most difficult* _____

_____   _____

_____   _____

_____   _____

1. I finished in two minutes! This computer game puzzle is _____ we have tried this semester.

2. You're awesome! Your score is _____ ever!

3. Which smartphone has _____ volume control?

4. My old phone had _____ screen quality! I couldn't see any texts at night!

5. That free download app is _____ I have ever tried—I can't get past level one!

9 **Read the e-mail.** Write a reply.

Hi!
    I'm doing a survey about computer games, websites, and apps.
Can you please take a moment to answer these questions?
    What are the best / worst / funniest / most useful / least exciting
computer games, websites, and apps that you know? Please explain why.
Thank you!
JJ

_____

_____

_____

_____

Mobile Magic!

[1] What connects government offices in Nigeria, doctors in Malawi, and farmers in El Salvador? The answer is . . . useful mobile phone software invented by Ken Banks. In Africa, Ken noticed that people in rural areas traveled for hours to share information. Because people there are not connected to the Internet, he decided cell phones could help.

[2] All you need is a laptop computer and a cell phone. It doesn't have to be the newest smartphone. An old or recycled phone is fine. "After downloading the free software, you never need the Internet again," Ken explains. Attach your phone to the laptop, type your message on the computer keyboard, select the people you want to contact, and hit "Send". The message goes to cell phones as a text!

[3] So what do people send messages about? One good example is in Malawi. Ken sent a hundred recycled phones and a laptop with his software downloaded. After training for two weeks, doctors in the city can communicate with rural villages to decide which medical supplies to bring on their visits. These texts save time and thousands of dollars in travel costs. Even more importantly, a group of doctors in Malawi can now help the highest number of patients ever.

[4] Ken tells us, "We need to help people recognize that you can do useful things without lots of money or expensive technology."

Read. Answer the questions.

1. Which continent gave Ken the idea to design mobile phone software?

   _____

2. How many times do you need to connect to the Internet to access this service?

   _____

3. Give two examples of how Ken's invention can help people in Africa.

   _____

   _____

12 **Write.** Choose the main idea for each paragraph from the box and write it in the chart. Then complete the chart with the details A–F. Write the letters in the spaces.

How it works	Ken's message	One example	Introduction

A. Type a message on the laptop.
B. Africans travel for hours to share information.
C. Thousands of hours and travel costs are saved, and many more patients are helped.
D. They are not connected to the Internet, but phones might help.
E. Click "Send" and the message goes to cell phones in a text.
F. Doctors send messages to mobile phones in rural villages.

	Main idea	Details
Paragraph 1		**1.** Nigeria, Malawi, El Salvador use Ken's text software. **2.** ____ **3.** ____
Paragraph 2		**1.** Connect phone to laptop. **2.** ____ **3.** ____
Paragraph 3		**1.** Malawi doctors received 100 phones, 1 laptop, and training. **2.** ____ **3.** ____
Concluding sentence		We don't need a lot of money or technology to be useful.

13 **Think about the information from the reading text.** You've read about a useful text message service. Check (✓) the sentences that are true.

☐ Only two or three countries can use the text service.

☐ Someone needs to type a message on a laptop.

☐ It saves people a lot of traveling time.

☐ It's only useful for doctors.

☐ Mobile phones can receive text messages.

GRAMMAR

Will and ***going to*: Talking about the future**

Schools **will have** chat rooms where students can ask questions online to teachers.	Wi-Fi **is going to speed up** in developing countries.
Smartphones **won't cost** so much money.	The Internet **isn't going to replace** teachers.
Will there **be** more female computer game designers? **Yes**, I think there **will be**.	**Are** our screens **going to affect** our eyesight? We**'re going to need** better eye tests.

To make predictions about the future, we use *will* or *going to*.
Will + verb: *will be, will go, will cost*
present form of *be* + *going to* + verb: *am/is/are* going to have
will not = won't
will = 'll

14 **Listen.** Circle the form of the verb that you hear. TR: 34

1. South Korea **is going to be / will be** a world leader in digital technology.

2. India **is going to build / will build** many new Wi-Fi towers.

3. Estonia **will continue to be / is going to be** very involved in the digital age.

4. Some experts say that many more countries **will enter / are going to enter** the race for the best designs in mobile technology.

5. Village farmers **are going to pay for / will pay for** services with their smartphones.

6. More people **are going to use / will use** taxis because it's easier to order one through the Internet.

15 **Listen.** Check the pictures that match the names you hear. TR: 35

1. 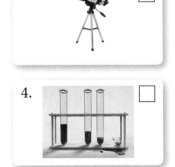 ☐

2.  ☐

3.  ☐

4. ☐

5.  ☐

6.  ☐

16 Read the blog. Circle the correct answers.

> ¹ Learning from our own mistakes is useful, but learning from another country's mistakes is going to be the fastest way to develop, I say.
>
> ² India has been developing its technology for many years. Other countries may have started before us, but today they often still have old technology— for example, unmodernized telephone systems. We can learn from this. First, we need to look at the original technology. We'll look at the problems but keep the best designs. But then we'll search for the latest ideas and create something similar but better. Countries like India are catching up. But there's competition! Some experts say that Estonia is going to be the most creative country for gadgets, and India will jump ahead with mobile phone technology.
>
> ³ How will India jump in front? For example, now most people in India go shopping in street markets and small, local shops. There aren't any large supermarkets in rural areas, so people have to travel to buy more expensive products. But soon we'll start to buy things using the Internet on our smartphones. We're still going to use our small shops and markets, but we'll "jump" over the need for supermarkets. Get ready— change will come fast!

1. What does the writer think is going to be the best way to improve her country?
   a. Learning from another country's mistakes   b. Making mistakes
   c. Copying old technology

2. How will countries like India design new gadgets and technology?
   a. They will keep the same old technology.
   b. They will copy and improve on existing technology.
   c. They won't spend any time on new ideas.

3. According to the blog, which country is going to design the most creative gadgets?
   a. Estonia   b. India   c. Britain

4. How will India "jump in front" of more developed countries?
   a. India will spend more money on travel.
   b. Indians won't use the Internet.
   c. Indians will use technology to develop smart solutions to everyday problems.

17 Write. Read the text in Activity 16 again. Write about some of the ideas in the text in your own words, using *will* and *going to*.

_____

_____

_____

WRITING

To write a good review of a product, we need descriptive words. We want our readers to imagine the product clearly. Details are important, so remember to list good and bad things about the product, and give examples of each.

18 Organize

1. Your topic is to write a review of a product that you have used. Look through the unit for product ideas, or do some research on the Internet, then think of similar products you have used.

2. Plan your writing. Your review needs examples of good and bad points. Finish with your opinion and the reasons that support it.

Use the chart to help you plan. List the examples you will use in your review.

Product	
Good points	
Bad points	
Your opinion and reasons	

19 Write

1. Go to p. 123 in your book. Reread the model and writing prompt.

2. Write your first draft. Check for organization, content, punctuation, capitalization, and spelling.

3. Write your final draft. Share it with your teacher and classmates.

Now I Can . . .

talk about cool apps and gadgets.

☐ Yes, I can!
☐ I think I can.
☐ I need more practice.

Write two sentences about apps and gadgets. Give examples of what they can do.

_____

_____

use superlatives to talk about extremes.

☐ Yes, I can!
☐ I think I can.
☐ I need more practice.

Complete the conversation with the superlatives.

Example: Your music app is (+/cool) _____*the coolest*_____ I have seen!

Pietro: Have you heard (+/new) _____ download from this band?

Camilla: No! Do you think it's their (+/good) _____ version?

Pietro: Well, we could look up a review to see (+/high) _____ rated downloads.

Camilla: OK, but that band is my (-/favorite) _____ . Can we look up this other band as well?

talk about the future using *will* and *going to*.

☐ Yes, I can!
☐ I think I can.
☐ I need more practice.

Write about the photo using *will* and *going to*.

_____

_____

write a review.

☐ Yes, I can!
☐ I think I can.
☐ I need more practice.

Write about a product. Include examples of its good and bad points, as well as your opinion about the product.

_____

_____

_____

Choose an activity. Go to p. 96.

Unit 8
Into the Past

1 **Draw.** Combine the words in the bones to make a question. Write the question on the first line. Answer the question using two of the words from the word bank. Write your answer on the second line.

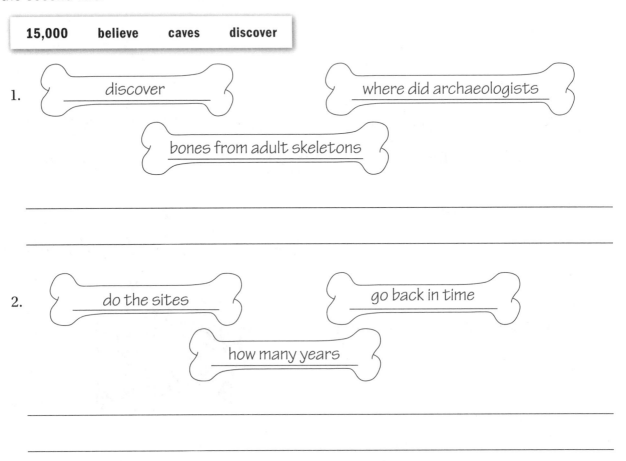

| 15,000 | believe | caves | discover |

1. discover | where did archaeologists

bones from adult skeletons

_____

_____

2. do the sites | go back in time

how many years

_____

_____

2 **Write.** Match the words and phrases with similar meanings. Then use the words or phrases to complete the sentences.

1. bones   a. ancestors

2. continue to think   b. skull

3. origins   c. still believe

Experts put together a human (1) _____ and some skeletal
(2) _____ .

Some scientists (3) _____ that the (4) _____
of American people are Asian, but others (5) _____ a different
story about their (6) _____ .

78

3 **Listen.** Complete the summary using the words in the box. **TR: 36**

adult	advanced	ancestors	believe
bones	discovered	skeleton	skull

Scientists _____ that they have _____ the origins of the American people.

The answer came from a nearly complete _____ found in the sea near Mexico. It belonged to a young woman, almost an _____ . The _____ show that she was a type of early human. Scientists used _____ computers to make a model head from the _____ bones and now think that the common _____ of the first Americans may have come from Asia.

4 **Write.** Use the words from Activity 3 and the box below to make sentences.

there + be	has/have + discover/believe

_____

_____

_____

_____

_____

_____

GRAMMAR

Present perfect: Describing a past action that still continues

Chess **has been** popular for hundreds of years.
I **have played** chess for five years.
My brother **hasn't played** board games since he started playing video games.
Have you always **liked** video games? Yes, I **have**.
How long **have** you **played** video games?

We use the present perfect to talk about actions that began in the past but continue in the present.

To form the present perfect, use *have* or *has* and a past participle of the verb. Most verbs form the past participle by adding –ed, but some verbs are irregular. (*be* → *been*, *go* → *gone*)

We use *for* with the present perfect to talk about how long it has been from the moment an action or situation began until the present moment.

For + period of time: **for** *two years,* **for** *five days,* **for** *a very long time*

We use *since* with the present perfect to talk about when an action or situation began.

Since + a point in time: **since** *last week,* **since** *2015,* **since** *I arrived*

5 **Complete the sentences.** Write the correct form of the verb in parentheses and select *for* or *since*.

1. My father _____ (play) chess _____ (for/since) 40 years.

2. My two brothers _____ (play) chess _____ (for/since) they were little, too.

3. I _____ (play) chess _____ (for/since) just one year, but it _____ (become) my favorite game!

4. My father _____ never _____ (like) video games, but my mother _____ always _____ (love) them.

5. I never liked video games, but that _____ (change) _____ (for/since) last week. I _____ (discover) a really cool video game about ancient Rome.

6. I only started to play a week ago, but I _____ (complete) all levels!

6 **Listen.** Circle the sentence with the present-perfect form. **TR: 37**

1.

    a. They discovered bones in a cave.

    b. They've drawn a map showing the bones in the cave.

    c. They show the map of the cave to the newspapers.

2.

    a. Scientists have studied early civilizations similar to our ancestors.

    b. Scientists believe that modern humans are less healthy.

    c. Our ancestors slept better than us.

3.

    a. Rajiv moved his queen three squares closer to Amena's king.

    b. Amena hasn't forgotten that the queen is a powerful chess piece.

    c. Amena blocks Rajiv's queen with another piece.

7 **Listen again.** Complete the sentences with the present-perfect form of the verb. **TR: 37**

1. First, they found bones in the cave. Next, they drew a map of the cave to show the newspapers. The journalists (see) _____ the map now.

2. Our ancestors slept very well. Modern humans don't sleep very well. Scientists (find) _____ that early civilizations can help us understand our sleep problems.

3. Rajiv moved his queen closer to Amena's king. Amena knows that the queen is a powerful chess piece. Rajiv (not win) _____ the chess game yet.

8 **Write.** Use the words to make sentences using the present perfect.

1. Experts are looking for descendants of the last King of India. They / find / some descendants / in Myanmar and Pakistan / but / most / live / India all their lives.

_____

2. Archaeologists in Russia / discover / unusually long skulls / site named Arkaim.

_____

9 **Listen and read.** As you read, think about what scientists have learned about ancient civilizations. **TR: 38**

My History Page

Wait—change the history books!
Which is the oldest civilization in Southeast Asia?

[1] For many years, scientists have thought that the oldest human species in Southeast Asia was from India, because humans have lived there for at least 10,000 years. Scientists believed that those early people moved east, and that their descendants populated other countries, such as my country, Sri Lanka. So this is what our education system has always taught teenagers like me.

[2] But new technology shows that there has been civilization in ancient Sri Lanka for much longer, dating back 30,000 years. Since the 1980s, archaeologists have studied skeletons that show cultures have survived almost three times longer than we previously believed. Finger bones and skulls discovered in archaeological sites in dry caves show that the ancestors of modern Sri Lankans were advanced enough to make their homes in caves 30,000 years ago. That's 20,000 years before people in Europe did this!

[3] So Sri Lankans now have new information about our origins. We have learned that our ancestors were almost the first humans to use tools to cut stone and hunt animals. I say "almost the first" because Sri Lankans are not the oldest civilization in the world. That prize goes to South Africa, where people have lived for an amazing 50,000 years! As technology improves, scientists must keep looking to see if they really have discovered the oldest sites in your country, too.

10 **Read again.** Answer the questions.

1. Which country did experts think had the oldest human civilization in Southeast Asia?

   _____

2. How many years have civilizations lived in Sri Lanka? _____

3. What were the ancient Sri Lankans doing 20,000 years before the Europeans?

   _____

4. Which country has the oldest civilization in the world? _____

11 Read. Match the cause with the effect. Write the number on the line.

Cause

1. Experts thought that India was the oldest civilization in Southeast Asia.

2. Scientists discovered bones from 30,000 years ago in Sri Lanka.

3. Scientists used modern technology to find the age of the bones.

Effect

_____ Now there are plans to search for older sites in other countries, too.

_____ So schools taught that Sri Lankans were descendants of Indians.

_____ So now we know there have been Sri Lankan civilizations for much longer.

12 Write. Read the text again. Write the cause and three possible effects in the graphic organizer. Write the letters in the spaces.

A. Archaeologists might search for older sites in other countries, too.

B. Scientists discovered 30,000-year-old bones in Sri Lanka.

C. Sri Lankan school books may need rewriting!

D. Europeans have learned that their ancestors are younger than Sri Lankans' ancestors.

cause _____ → effect _____ / effect _____ / effect _____

13 Write. In this unit, you have read about the origins of civilizations and the changing lives of young people. Write possible effects for these causes.

1. Cause: The Aztec education system taught boys and girls separate subjects.

   Effect: _____

2. Cause: Archaeologists don't always use the most modern technology in every country.

   Effect: _____

3. Cause: Many centuries ago, most adults could not read or write.

   Effect: _____

4. Cause: Some poor teenagers worked in factories in England in the 1800s.

   Effect: _____

GRAMMAR

There + to be: **Expressing existence at different points of time**

There was going to be a talk about teenage art and culture tonight.	But unfortunately, **there isn't** anybody available to speak at the moment.
In any teenager's life **there are** always good times and bad times.	**Were there** difficult times for you, too? Yes, **there've been** many!
At the camp **there'll be** chores for us to do every day.	**There's been** a tradition that the teachers all cook breakfast for us.

To show that something exists in our world we use *there + be: there is/was, there are/were, there has/have been, there will be, there is/are going to be,* etc.
There can be followed by a singular or plural form of the verb *be.* The choice of singular or plural depends on the noun that comes after the verb.
For questions, the form of *be* is placed before *there.*

14 **Listen.** Circle the correct form of *be.* **TR: 39**

1. There **is / are / were** a lot of missing pieces in this chess set.

2. There **were / will be / are** too many people at the festival.

3. Did you say there **will be / was / is** a traditional dance?

4. In next year's exhibition there **will be / are going to be / have been** some bones from 2,000 years ago!

5. There **have been / are / will be** giant stones here for ages!

6. Someone has moved my pieces. There **was / is / were** an empty space here before!

7. You said there **aren't / won't be / weren't** any pieces for this game, but I've found some!

8. The king's descendants are still alive. There **were / is / are** six grandchildren in India.

15 **Read.** Match the graph to the sentence. Write A, B, or C.

A. There was very little education for girls one hundred years ago.

B. There has been an increase in primary-school-aged girls in school.

C. In the future we hope that there will be more girls in schools. _____

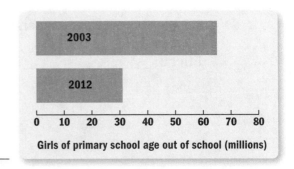

Girls of primary school age out of school (millions)

16 **Write.** Read the conversations and write *there* + the correct form of *be* in the spaces.

1. Is there a spinner for this game?

   Yes, _____*there's*_____ a special spinner with pictures instead of numbers.

2. Are there any ancient sites here?

   No, unfortunately _____ any ancient sites to visit.

3. Has there been any interest from the newspapers about this new site?

   There's been a little. _____ a few questions from a local magazine, but
   we haven't contacted all of the newspapers yet.

17 **Read and listen.** Check **T** for *True* and **F** for *False*. **TR: 40**

Carrom: An ancient game

The board Carrom is a game that's played on a smooth, flat,
wooden board. In each corner there's a circular hole about
2 in. (5 cm) in diameter, and underneath each hole there's
a net pocket to catch the pieces.

The pieces Each player has a "striker" piece about 2 in. in diameter. There are also nine dark
pieces and nine light pieces, plus a red piece called the "Queen." People often have their own
strikers, which are sometimes made of bone and so are heavier than the wooden pieces.

Preparation The Queen is placed in the center of the board. Six pieces form a circle around
the Queen. The remaining twelve pieces go around the first circle of six pieces.

Objective Players choose their color and then take turns pushing their striker piece against
the other pieces. The goal is to get your pieces into the corner pockets. The winner is the
player who has put all his or her pieces in the pockets first. However, it's not just a simple race.
Neither player wins until one player has put the Queen in a pocket, too.

	T	F
1. On a Carrom board there are round holes in each corner.	☐	☐
2. There are 20 pieces, including two strikers and the Queen.	☐	☐
3. The heaviest piece in Carrom is the striker.	☐	☐
4. Players use their strikers to push their pieces into the holes at the corners.	☐	☐
5. The game ends when there are no pieces on the board but the Queen.	☐	☐

18 **Write.** Reread the description of Carrom. Then write a short paragraph describing a board
game you know and enjoy playing.

19 Organize

1. Your topic is to describe a traditional festival or celebration from your culture. Decide on your topic. Decide how to divide your topic into two or three parts.

2. Plan your writing. Research the topic. You'll need an introductory topic sentence. Your topic sentence will describe the festival or celebration. Write your topic sentence here:

   _____

   Next, you'll need to add details for each part of your paragraph. Make a list of details for each part.

   _____

   _____

   _____

   _____

   Remember to finish your paragraph with a conclusion. Write your concluding sentence here:

   _____

   _____

20 Write

1. Go to p. 139 in your book. Reread the model and writing prompt.

2. Write your first draft. Check for organization, content, punctuation, capitalization, and spelling.

3. Write your final draft. Share it with your teacher and classmates.

Now I Can . . .

talk about events in the past.

Describe something that happened last month or last year.
Write two or three sentences.

☐ Yes, I can!
☐ I think I can.
☐ I need more practice.

_____

_____

_____

describe actions that started in the past and continue into the present.

☐ Yes, I can!
☐ I think I can.
☐ I need more practice.

Complete the sentences using verbs in the present-perfect form.

1. Many people from Kenya (continue) _____ winning prizes in international sports competitions.

2. One researcher (discover) _____ that teaching chess is helpful in many areas of education.

3. Surprisingly, when observing less advanced civilizations, we (learn) _____ more about our own culture.

express existence at different points of time using _there + to be_.

☐ Yes, I can!
☐ I think I can.
☐ I need more practice.

Complete the sentences with _there + to be_.

1. We saw that _____ bones from adult skeletons in the cave.

2. I have a question: _____ any chores to do at the education camp next week?

3. I don't think _____ _____ a black queen piece in this old chess set.

write a classification paragraph.

☐ Yes, I can!
☐ I think I can.
☐ I need more practice.

Describe a game.

_____

_____

_____

Choose an activity. Go to p. 96.

Units 7–8 Review

1 **Read.** Choose the correct word to complete the sentences.

1. I've looked up the word ____ on the Internet, and it says it's a blood relative, for example a child born to a parent, connected to older ancestors.
   a. "advanced" b. "civilization" c. "descendant"

2. Can you please ____ the game? I've waited 5 minutes for my turn already!
   a. discover b. continue c. believe

3. Can you believe the Wi-Fi here? I've downloaded the complete video already! It's the ____ Internet access in town!
   a. fast b. faster c. fastest

4. These gadgets use too much power. My ____ has died already after only an hour!
   a. microphone b. battery c. screen

5. My art project ____ fun. We'll design new king and queen chess pieces.
   a. is going to be b. are going to be c. will

6. Have you seen the smartphones with the Chinese ____ app? You can type in Chinese.
   a. find b. camera c. keyboard

2 **Listen.** Number the pictures in the order you hear them described in the radio show. Then listen again and answer the questions. **TR: 41**

Year of the Rooster

____ ____ ____

1. What is another name for the Chinese New Year festival?

_____

2. Which digital Chinese New Year apps have people downloaded?

_____

3. What have been traditional New Year gifts in the past?

_____

3 **Read.** Decide which answer (*a*, *b*, or *c*) is <u>not</u> true. Circle the letter.

> Dear Barbara,
>
> There's going to be a festival in our village next summer! Will you be free to visit? I've joined the festival planning group, so it'll be more exciting for teenagers. Before, only adults decided on the food and music, and there weren't any games. I've started to search the Internet for the most interesting festival games and music. Last year there was a local band. They weren't the best but they were fun. This year the music is going to be even better—I'm the DJ! Please send any helpful advice you have, and any suggestions for music downloads!
>
> Check your calendar—it's going to be incredible!
>
> Hope to see you soon,
>
> Mike

1. Mike asks his friend Barbara
   a. to visit his village festival next summer.
   b. to be a DJ at the festival.
   c. to help him choose music.

2. Last year
   a. there weren't any games.
   b. the adults chose the entertainment.
   c. there was Mexican food.

3. Mike thinks that
   a. the local band was the worst thing at the festival.
   b. DJ music will be more exciting for teenagers.
   c. the festival will be better next summer.

4. Barbara
   a. was asked to send ideas about the music.
   b. was asked to give advice to Mike.
   c. is going to be in the festival planning group.

4 **Write.** Reread Mike's e-mail in Activity 3 and write a reply. Ask questions about the events last year and the events planned for this year. Use the present perfect, *will*, and *going to* questions.

_____

_____

_____

Choose an activity

1 Use words from the list to talk about life in one of your favorite places.

highway	indoor	land		outdoor
park	rural	surrounded by		unique
unusual	urban			

2 Use simple-present verbs you know and the words in the list to make positive and negative statements about a place you know.

architecture	concrete	construct	design
land	live	plan	

_____

_____

_____

_____

3 Complete each sentence using your own ideas. Use *in* or *on* in each sentence.

This skyscraper is unusual because it has

_____

That tower is unique. It

_____

That park is a new design. It

_____

4 **Work in pairs.** Interview an architect.

- Research an architect.
- Prepare three questions about the buildings she or he designs. Make notes about the answers to your questions.
- Assign the roles of interviewer and architect.
- Practice the interview.
- Act out the interview in class, or use a phone or tablet to make a video.

5 **Write.** Think of a place that makes you happy. Describe it.

- To plan your writing, follow the steps on p. 10 of your workbook.
- Share your writing with your teacher and classmates.

6 **Write.** You see this poster on a local notice board.

> **Design Competition**
>
> *Local residents, now you can help to plan your capital city! This is a unique chance to give architects your ideas about urban spaces and the architecture you're surrounded by. Do you have any unusual ideas for bridges, towers, skyscrapers, or sidewalks?*

Send an e-mail to a friend describing your ideas. Write at least 100 words.

Choose an activity

1 Connect words from the two word boxes to talk about careers.

advisor	archaeologist	photographer
researcher	scientist	

adventure	dangerous	explore
office	passion	schedule

2 Use simple-present verbs to ask and answer questions. Use words from the list.

apply for	commute	consider	create
explore	study	take risks	train

3 Complete each sentence with a possessive.

We left _____ plans on the table. Please bring them here.

The photographer can't find _____ camera. Is it in your office?

Two researchers need to apply for _____ jobs again. Let's interview them next week.

Look at that building! _____ shape is very unusual.

I love _____ job. I explore underwater caves.

4 **Work in pairs.** Have a conversation about work. Repeat the activity in class, or make a video on your phone or tablet.

Tell your partner about someone you know who has an interesting job and the work they do. Include:

- the name of the job
- where he or she works
- what he or she does
- special skills
- any special study or training.

5 **Write.** Think of an unusual career you know something about. Describe it. Where does it take place? What's hard about it. What's fun?

- To plan your writing, follow the steps on p. 20 of your workbook.
- Share your writing with your teacher and classmates.

6 **Write.** Your friend sends you a message.

Dangerous jobs?

Hi,

This week my school project is about difficult careers. I think unusual—and even dangerous—jobs are interesting, don't you? Do know anything about dangerous or unusual jobs?

Reply and describe your ideas. Write at least 100 words.

Choose an activity

1 Describe things that happen during the day and at night. Use words from the list.

darkness	fascinate	glow
go to sleep	light up	nocturnal
observe	streetlight	

2 Use action and non-action verbs to describe the things in the word box.

Example: *At dawn we see the sunrise. The sun is rising now, and I'm watching it!*

dawn	daylight	festival
headlights	horizon	streetlights
sunrise	sunset	time zones

3 You received a text message from a cousin who just moved to your neighborhood.. Answer the questions using *at*, *on*, or *in*.

Hi! Sorry to text again, but I forgot to ask you some questions.

When are you home?

What time do you go to sleep?

In the mornings, are you usually awake when it's still dark?

When is the best time to call you? Evenings? Saturday mornings?

Also, I want to take photos of my new house and the view. When is the sunset tonight?

See you at school!

4 **Work in pairs.** You want to walk to your friend's house after dark. Your parents don't like the idea. Role-play the dialogue.

- Choose roles (yourself, your mom or dad).
- Think about the road, the sidewalk, the streetlights, the car headlights, and the time.
- Practice the dialogue. Change roles, and practice the dialogue again
- Assign final roles.
- Act out the dialogue in class, or use a phone or tablet to make a video.

5 **Write.** Think of an event that usually happens at night. Use sense words to describe the event.

- To plan your writing, follow the steps on p. 32 of your workbook.
- Share your writing with your teacher and classmates.

6 **Write.** Your teacher asks you to write a story. This is the title of the story.

My Five Senses Saved Me!

Write your story. Write at least 160 words.

Choose an activity

1 Spin a paperclip to choose words from the circle. Use the words you land on to make sentences about wildlife.

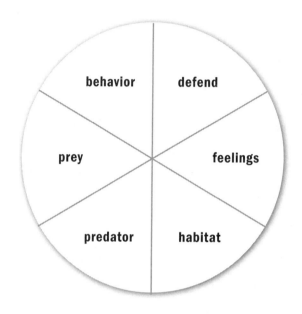

behavior defend

prey feelings

predator habitat

2 Give advice to young people about living together with wildlife. Use words from the list and *must*, *should/shouldn't*, and *have/has to* or *do/doesn't have to*.

afraid of	avoid	frighten
hunt	learn	mistreat
rescue	survive	

3 Think of a predator you know about. What is its prey? Use *can*, *can't*, *could*, and *couldn't* to describe its behavior.

4 **Work in pairs.** Plan an interview with an animal conservationist.

- Research a conservationist who works with animals.
- List several things about his or her work that interest you.
- Prepare three questions about his or her work. Make notes about the answers to your questions.
- Choose roles and practice the interview with a partner.
- Act out the conversation in class, or use a smartphone or tablet to make a video.

5 **Write.** Think about someone you know. Then choose an unusual animal. Imagine a scene in which they interact. The scene can be realistic, or it can be a fantasy.

- To plan your writing, follow the steps on p. 42 of your workbook.
- Share your writing with your teacher and classmates.

6 **Write.** Read the advertisement. Then write an e-mail.

Photo Story

Are you a good photographer? We need amazing photos that show relationships between people and unusual animals.

Write an e-mail to a person who interacts with an unusual animal. Describe your ideas for a photo story. Write at least 100 words.

Choose an activity

☐ **1** Complete the quiz about fashion. Then write two more questions for your classmates.

1. Which fabric is strong, practical, and blue?

   _____

2. When a jacket and pants are made from the same fabric, we call it a _____ .

3. Many people wear these at school or work.

   _____

4. What can people wear to make them look taller? _____

☐ **2** Change the regular verbs in the box to the simple past. Then use the simple-past verbs to describe fashion through history.

decorate	dress up	look
paint	pierce	protect
replace	use	

☐ **3** Change the irregular verbs in the box to the simple past. Then use the simple-past verbs to describe fashion through history. Explain why people did those things.

have	put	think	wear

Example: *People wore headscarves because they wanted to be formal and protect their heads from the sun.*

☐ **4** **Work in pairs.** Take turns talking about clothes. Think of a piece of clothing. Describe it, but don't say its name. Can your partner guess?

Example: *It's casual. We wear it on our heads. It's good for playing sports. It's colorful. It might have the name of a sports team on it.* Answer: *baseball cap*

Repeat the activity in class, or make a video on your phone or tablet.

☐ **5** **Write.** Choose some clothes you like. Describe them.

- To plan your writing, follow the steps on p. 54 in your workbook.
- Illustrate and display your work for your classmates to read.

☐ **6** Your teacher asks you to design clothes for a drama project.

Dramatic Clothing

- Think about a movie character or a character from history, for example, Superman or Queen Elizabeth I.
- Describe his or her clothes. Remember to describe head gear, shoes, jewelry, and accessories.

Describe your ideas for your character's clothes. Write at least 100 words.

Choose an activity

1 Talk about the 21st-century music business. Use words from the list.

combine	download	edit
fan	hit	hybrid
imagine	imitate	mix
opinion	perform	record
song	version	video

2 Compare the pairs.

electronic music / traditional music

a live performance / an audio recording

CDs / downloads

original recording / cover version (copy)

Example: *I prefer original songs, not copies of the original. Original songs are simpler.*

3 Grandma calls you from the supermarket. Answer her questions about the shopping list. Use count and noncount nouns.

> Hello dear!
> Sorry, I forgot my shopping list. Please help. Is there some tomato sauce in the refrigerator? How much is there? Are there any cookies in the cabinet? Do I need butter? Coffee? Bread? Sugar?

4 **Work in pairs.** You want to make something completely new. Discuss ideas with a partner. Role-play the dialogue.

- Choose two things to mix together.
- Think about sports and games, music, animals, food, art, or fashion. Make a mash-up! What did you mash up? What is your new invention called?
- Practice the dialogue.
- Act out the dialogue in class, or use a phone or tablet to make a video.

5 **Write.** Use examples and details to describe a mash-up sport, food, type of fashion, music, or art.

- To plan your writing, follow the steps on p. 64 of your workbook.
- Show your writing to your teacher and classmates.

6 **Write.** Your teacher asks you to write about an example of a mash-up. This is the title you will use:

> **1 + 1 = 3?**
> **My mash-up!**

Write at least 100 words.

Choose an activity

1 **Work in pairs.** Put the words in the box in order from 1 to 5. (1 = the coolest and 5 = the least cool.) Explain your choices to a partner.

a computer game	a sports gadget	a music app
a tablet	a smartphone	

Now put the things in order of practicality, from the most to the least practical. Explain your thinking.

2 List several activities you plan to do next week. Are you going to do anything practical or interesting? Or maybe something incredible?

practical	interesting	incredible

3 **Write.** Choose a product that has positive and negative points. Describe its good and bad points, and then give your opinion.

- To plan your writing, follow the steps on p. 76 of your workbook.
- Share your writing with your teacher and classmates.

4 **Write.** Below is part of a letter from an English-speaking friend.

When I come to visit you, I want to buy something from your country. Maybe you can help me think of an idea. I want something interesting and unusual. It doesn't have to be perfect! If you think of anything, please tell me about the good and bad points. Then I can choose the best thing to buy.

Respond to the letter. Write at least 100 words.

1 How have archaeologists helped us learn about our world? Use words from the list. Make sentences using present-perfect verbs.

Example: *They have discovered bones under the sea.*

advanced	ancestors	bones	civilization
descendant	origins	site	skeleton
skull	species		

2 **Work in pairs.** Choose a word from Activity 1. Have a conversation about it using *there + be.* Repeat the activity in class, or make a video on a phone or tablet.

3 **Write.** Choose a game that you enjoy playing. Describe it in detail. Classify the different parts of the game.

- To plan your writing, follow the steps on p. 86 in your workbook.
- Share your writing with your teacher and classmates.

4 Below is part of an e-mail you received from an Australian friend.

Hello,

I'm writing a blog about Internet games for teenagers. Do you know any cool games? I'm thinking about games related to education or culture. I'm also interested in games that help with math or maybe language learning. I DON'T want to write about games that involve racing or fighting. Can you please help me by explaining your favorite educational Internet game?

Write a reply. Write at least 100 words.